MW00335801

Unfortunately this book is fiction;
would that parts of it at least were not.

P.W. 1986

The Second Earth

THE PENTATEUCH RE-TOLD

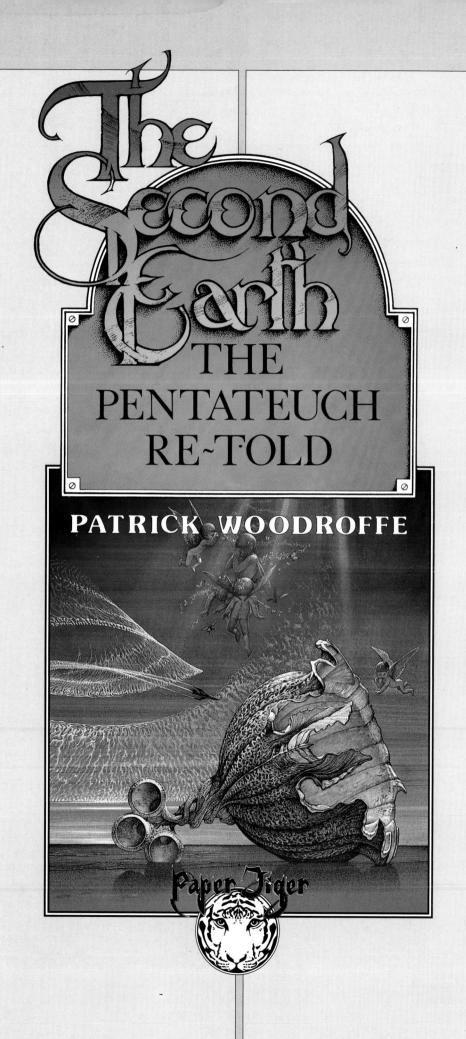

PATRICK WOODROFFE

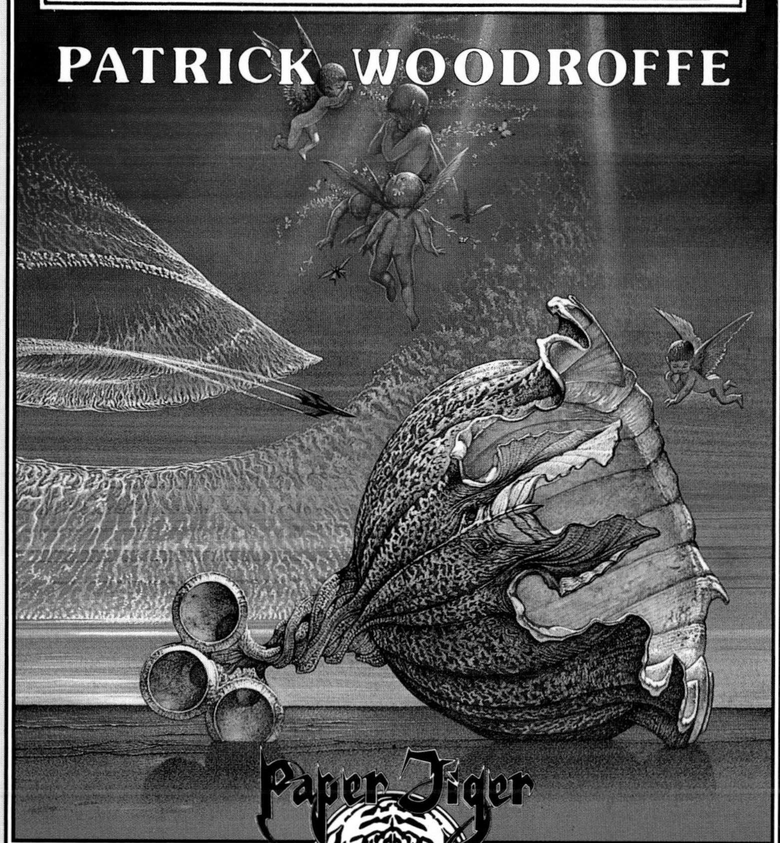

Paper Tiger

© Copyright text and illustrations
Patrick Woodroffe 1987

No part of this book may be reproduced in any form or by electronic or mechanical means, including information storage and retrieval systems, without prior written permission from Dragon's World Ltd. and from Patrick Woodroffe, except by reviewers who may quote brief passages in reviews.
All rights reserved.

Produced and designed by
Patrick Woodroffe.

Caution: All images are copyright by Patrick Woodroffe or by publishers acknowledged in the text. Their use in any form without prior written permission from Patrick Woodroffe or the appropriate copyright holder is strictly forbidden.

A DRAGON'S WORLD IMPRINT
Dragon's World Ltd
Limpsfield, Surrey RH8 0DY
Great Britain

First published 1987
Reprinted 1989

Hardback: ISBN 1 85028 042 8
Limpback: ISBN 1 85028 043 6

PRINTED IN SINGAPORE

The Second Earth

CONTENTS

With a lever to reach from the low to the high,
And the Earth as the pivot, a star as the guide,
Then maybe a baby could move the sky,
And even a minnow might turn the tide.

FOREWORD

ROGER DEAN

I have always been impressed by the fine craftsmanship of Patrick Woodroffe's work, so when I was asked to write a foreword for this book I was happy to be able to put into print those thoughts which are not so easily communicated over the telephone during a business conversation, and which are so easily overlooked because I have assumed that they are a part of a common understanding between respected colleagues.

I have already mentioned Patrick Woodroffe's craftsmanship. It seemed that this was the obvious place to start any discussion of his work. It is such a rare thing these days to be excited and even seduced by imagery which is the result of a genuine joy in the mastery of a number of media. It is perhaps most noticeably that aspect of his work which reflects and conveys his pleasure, curiosity and wonder at the limitless possibilities of creating two-dimensional images.

Craftsmanship and discipline are the means by which great art is achieved. There can be no such thing as great art without it. I am not discussing beauty; beauty and horror exist all around us and separate from us, all we have to do is to perceive it.

This is not so with art. Art has to be made, and made from something material. It is the product of consciousness, for the extension of consciousness, but it is also essentially the material product of the maker. It is not poetry, literature or music, it is not abstract in this sense, nor is it conceptual. It is matter, shaped, formed and described by the artist, and the artist's skill in making it is crucial; it is the difference between inspired work and the betrayal of the artist. This skill is not something that just arrives ready-made, it has to be developed. Even in the most gifted it only comes with disciplined study, constant practice and application over many years. This is the only way and there is no alternative. I am not, however, suggesting that technical facility alone is enough; it has to be allied to a creative consciousness. If you fail to train the hand, in its turn the hand will be unable to train the mind, and with that second failure goes any hope of enlightenment or deep understanding of the art form. The hand and brain should be able to work together without conscious intervention.

Art must be produced by skilled craftsmanship, but it does not have to be complex or laboured. However, a Zen master calligrapher is not a five-year-old child. These thoughts prompted by Patrick Woodroffe's work sound, on reflection, to be rather stiff and formal, not at all as I would have chosen to express myself. I discovered that in the process of writing this introduction that the element of skill which I admire in his work is something which generally seems to be out of favour at the moment. While Patrick Woodroffe's work may be many things to many people, to me it argues most effectively for a revival of interest in the possibilities that are only open to those who are courageous and adventurous enough to pursue with humility the skills of the artist/craftsman.

Patrick Woodroffe's visions, his particular flights of fancy are unimaginable without this craftsmanship. The intricate jewel-like oil paintings especially are quite wonderful.

As he also wrote the story, the whole book is a tribute to a fantastic imagination rendered with consummate skill.

Roger Dean 1987

The alien space-craft *Hermes* was discovered in 2378 — an event that changed the world.

PREFACE

Dr. Alexander M. Glover
Sec. Gen. U.N.T.W.
July 2387.

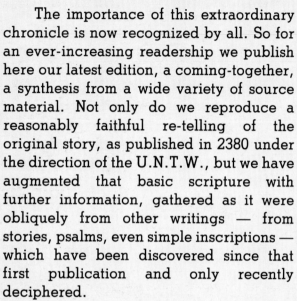

The importance of this extraordinary chronicle is now recognized by all. So for an ever-increasing readership we publish here our latest edition, a coming-together, a synthesis from a wide variety of source material. Not only do we reproduce a reasonably faithful re-telling of the original story, as published in 2380 under the direction of the U.N.T.W., but we have augmented that basic scripture with further information, gathered as it were obliquely from other writings — from stories, psalms, even simple inscriptions — which have been discovered since that first publication and only recently deciphered.

There is however, one obvious respect in which this new edition differs from the 2380 publication. Unfortunately the musical supplement has had to be excluded, mainly for reasons of economy. Perhaps in the near future we may be able to produce an even more complete revision, including perhaps even more of the music.

It was only in early 2379 that the story first broke. It is strange how long ago that all seems now. The discovery of a derelict space-craft, in orbit around Saturn, was remarkable enough in itself, but the consequential research has boosted our scientific knowledge like an injection of intellectual adrenalin.

And yet it was not the alien technology — the new insights into every branch of science, from inter-stellar ballistics to exo-biology — that excited the researchers of our *Project Hermes.* It was a set of a hundred or so metal tablets, each of them etched with strange ideographic inscriptions — an unimaginably ancient scripture lovingly preserved in an incongruous environment of high technology — it was this that surprised and fascinated us all.

And later, when the full significance of these and other writings was realized, we knew that this strange story was destined to affect every one of us. This alien PENTATEUCH would change the world.

Titan Base was established by U.N.T.W. in the year 2378, a scientific colony designed only to study the giant planet Saturn and its wonderful family of moons. They boasted the latest equipment for the detailed investigation of seismic phenomena, they had at their disposal atmospheric sondes of extreme sensitivity, they had drills for core-sampling research, remote-controlled exploratory robots, tugs, orbiters, landers — all the complex machinery of a typical modern research station. Yet because it had long ago been established that no life was to be expected — let alone evidence of civilisation — anywhere in the Saturnian system, they had with them no resources for dealing with exo-technology, exo-archaeology or even exo-biology. Saturn is still a long way from Earth. There was no time to wait for the real experts.

Civilization always was impatient, so the Commander-in-Chief of Titan Base, Pierre Marin Jnr., soon received our official permission from Earth Headquarters to send a preliminary medical team to investigate the huge space-derelict, to establish by the statutory BIOSCAN clearance technique whether or not it would be safe for a full team of investigators to board the ship. The great hulk was clearly very ancient indeed; the pock-marks on the fuselage testified at least to that. It was highly unlikely that the ship still contained any living creatures. It emitted no detectable energies on any wave-length, no light, no heat, no magnetic or radio activity whatsoever. It was clearly not only very ancient, but also utterly dead. And yet the formalities of BIOSCAN clearance must inevitably be adhered to. After the tragic demise of early expeditions to Mars and Venus, no risks could be taken where unknown pathogens might possibly linger.

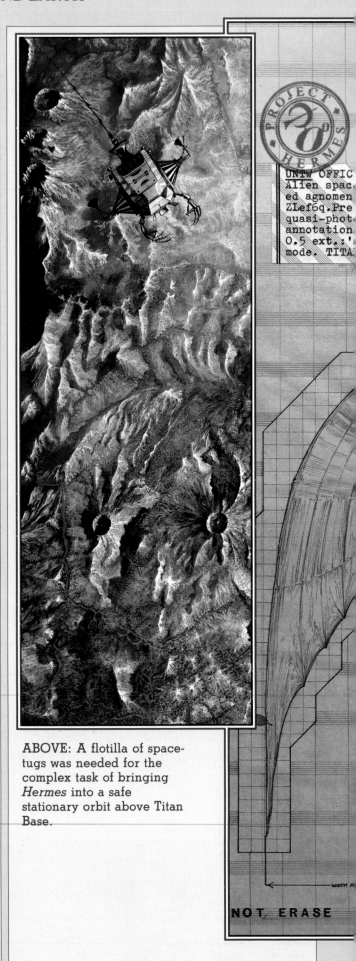

ABOVE: A flotilla of space-tugs was needed for the complex task of bringing *Hermes* into a safe stationary orbit above Titan Base.

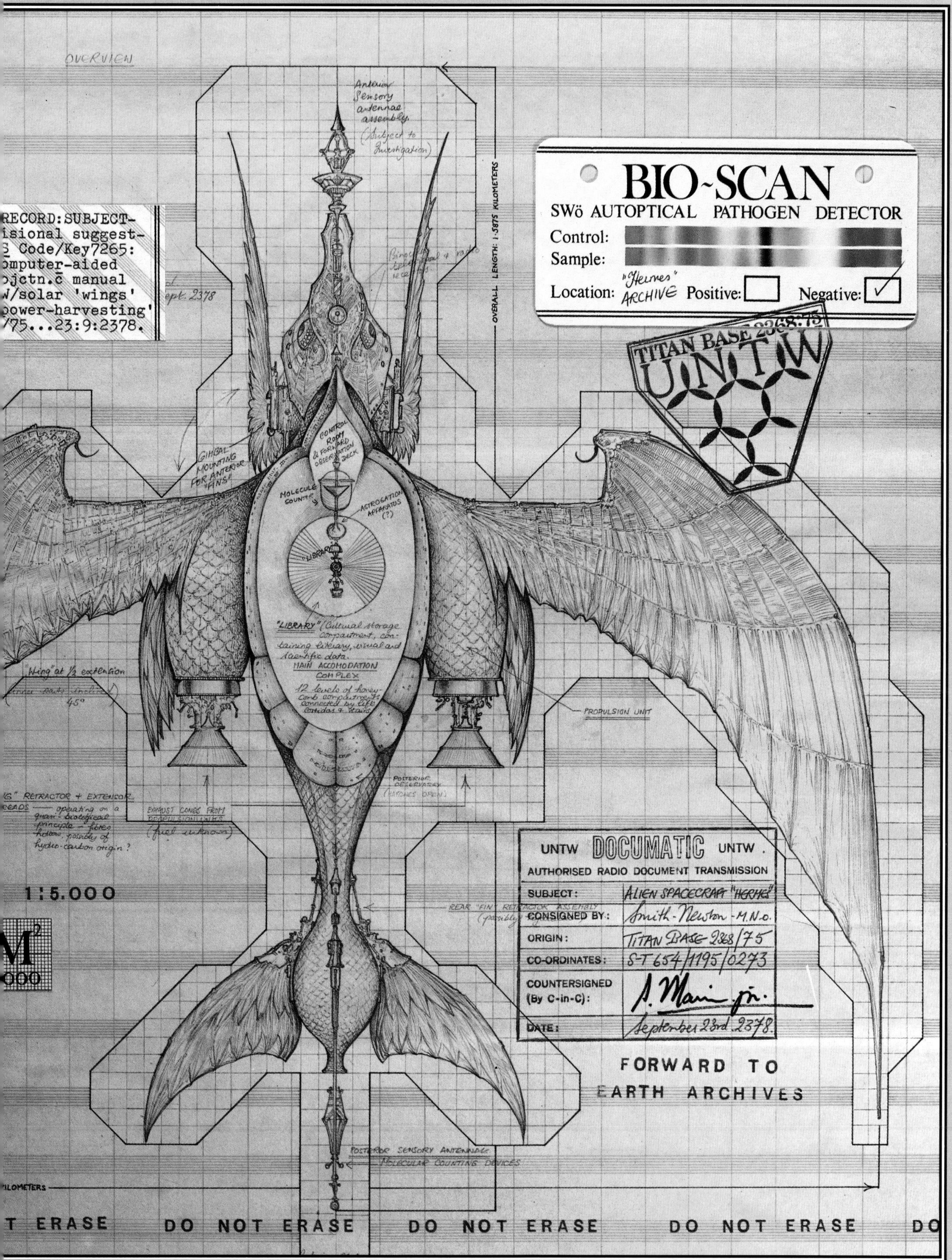

ABOVE: *Hermes* was obviously designed to imitate the shapes of both fish and bird. This drawing by Smith-Newton shows how the wings and fins could be extended for atmospheric flight.

Clearance was duly obtained. On September 20th 2378, the alien space-craft — though apparently of "bio-mechanical" construction, and therefore technically neither animal nor machine — was declared sterile. But strangely enough, not only sterile. It was also utterly deserted. Like the *Marie Celeste* of Earth, the alien ship had no crew, bearing no single clue — as yet — about the mysterious fate that had overcome her former masters.

Its size was prodigious, confusing the senses. It measured well over a kilometer from end to end. But I waste words. Surely by now all of you who read this will either have seen the ship for yourselves or at the very least have taken a detailed televisual guided tour. Yet no metaphor can adequately communicate the wonder which that unique discovery inspired in the hearts and minds of its first witnesses. It was, and is, the most remarkable archaeological discovery ever made.

And as we now know, it was not a true alien after all.

It was modelled — apparently deliberately — on the familiar shapes of fishes and birds. Its systems were, as I said, of a "bio-mechanical" nature, processes we even now do not fully understand. As it loomed majestically in space, untethered except by its invisible stationary orbit, it was impossible not to regard it as a living creature, or at least as a thing that had once lived.

The first reports were amazing. Excited documatics were transmitted immediately to Earth. Smith-Newton's seemingly fanciful drawings, consigned only three days after Bioscan clearance, were the first images ever seen on Earth of the oldest artifact ever discovered. It was hard to take in — so huge, so exotic, so unutterably ancient — and yet at the same time curiously familiar. The messenger had arrived. *Out of Darkness to the Second Earth.* The broken rainbow would be made whole.

Project Hermes had begun.

BELOW: For flight in the vacuum of space the wings and fins were furled. Propulsion was by a pair of rocket motors either side of the fuselage. Thrusters in the tail-assembly were apparently used to make fine course corrections.

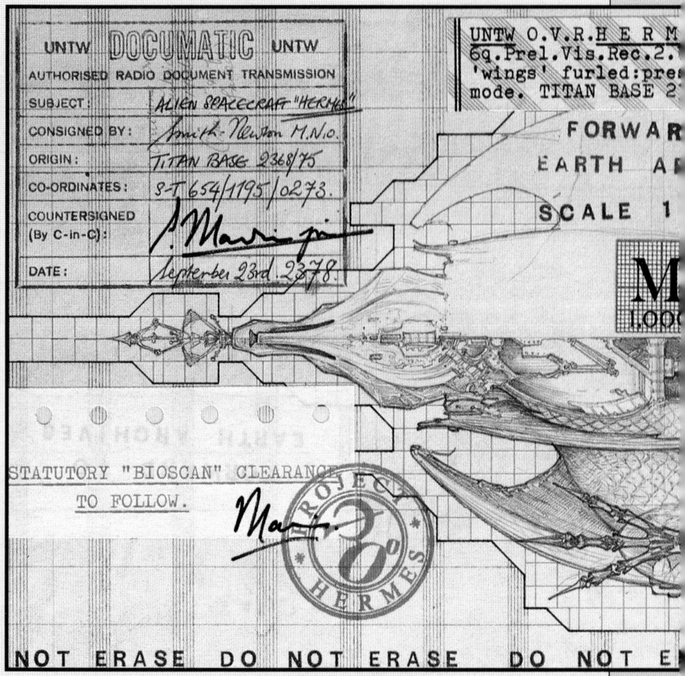

It was only to be expected that our own Greek mythology should as usual provide us with an adequately grandiose name for our project. Hermes was the messenger of the ancient Greek pantheon. If this ancient ship had a message for us, it seemed to be written in those mysterious tablets of ideographic scripture. The message did indeed seem to come from the gods themselves.

Curiously enough, Hermes' orbit around Saturn had reached a critical point. The timing seemed amazingly coincidental — too close for comfort. Was it possible that its masters had foreseen this? Was it part of their grand design? If we had waited only another five years before setting up our base on Titan, then this amazing space-derelict, along with all its priceless cargo, would have been drawn inexorably closer to Saturn, utterly destroyed by its inevitably decaying orbit. Probably for thousands of centuries, Hermes had stood as a beacon in space, waiting for the technology of man to come of age. Its masters left the archive open to the stars. For a billion years the book waited to be read.

RIGHT: *Hermes* with wings extended for flight in the atmosphere.

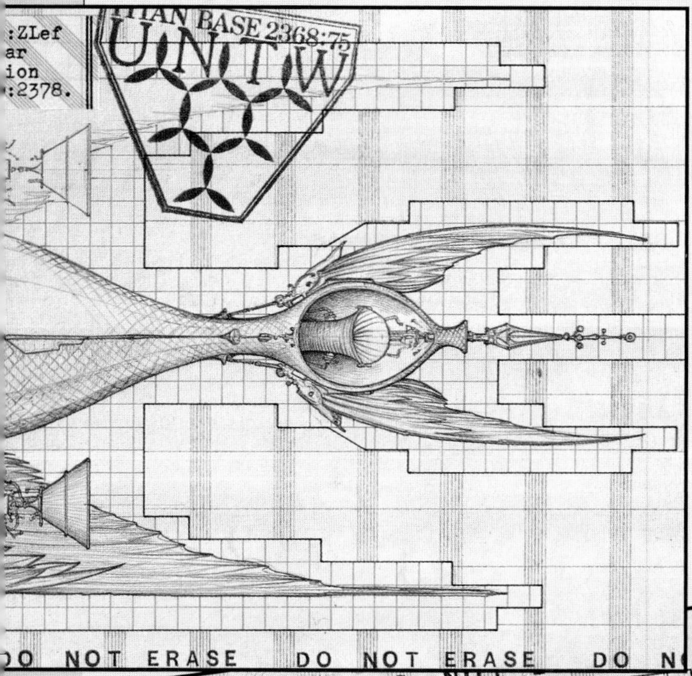

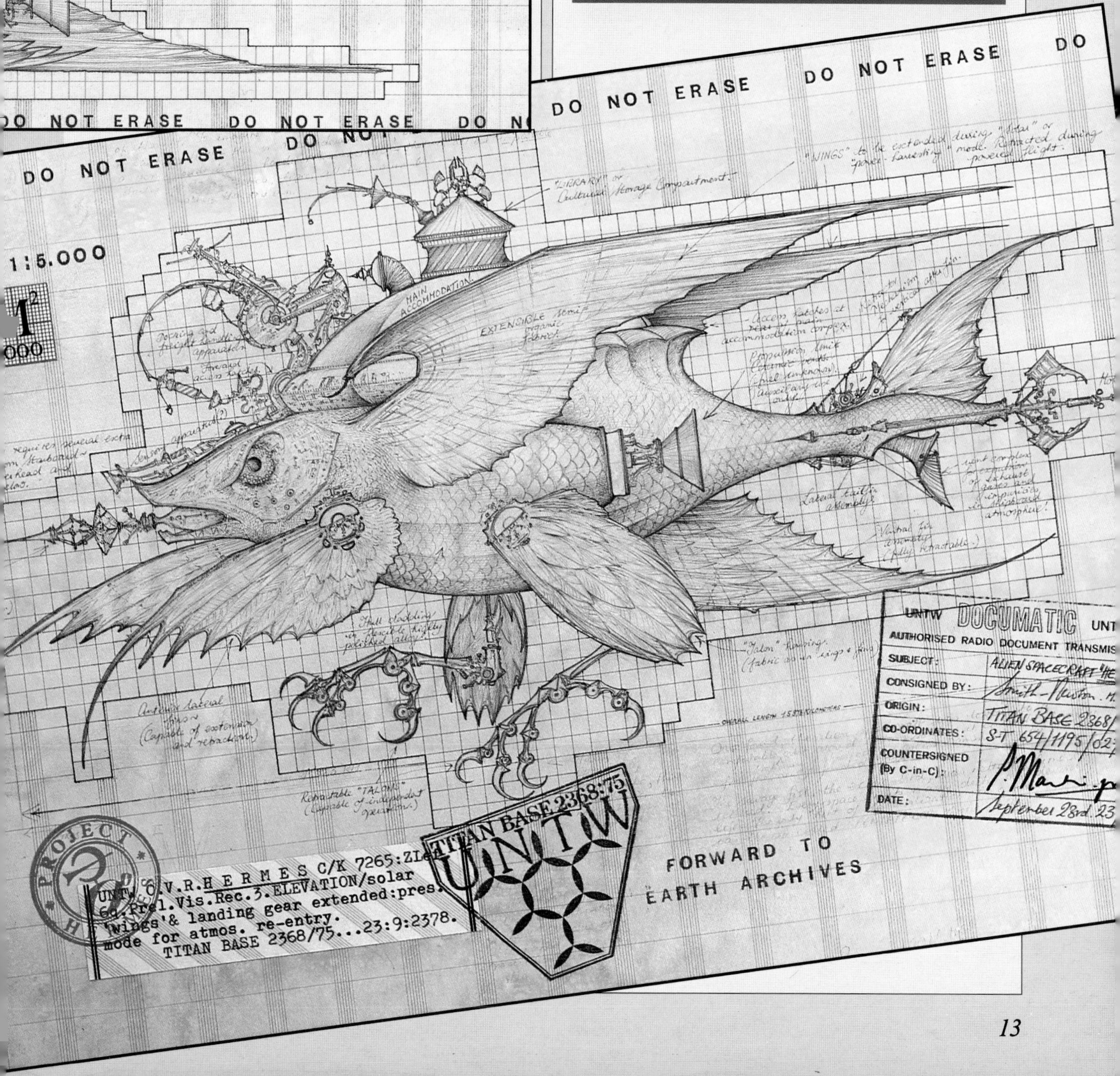

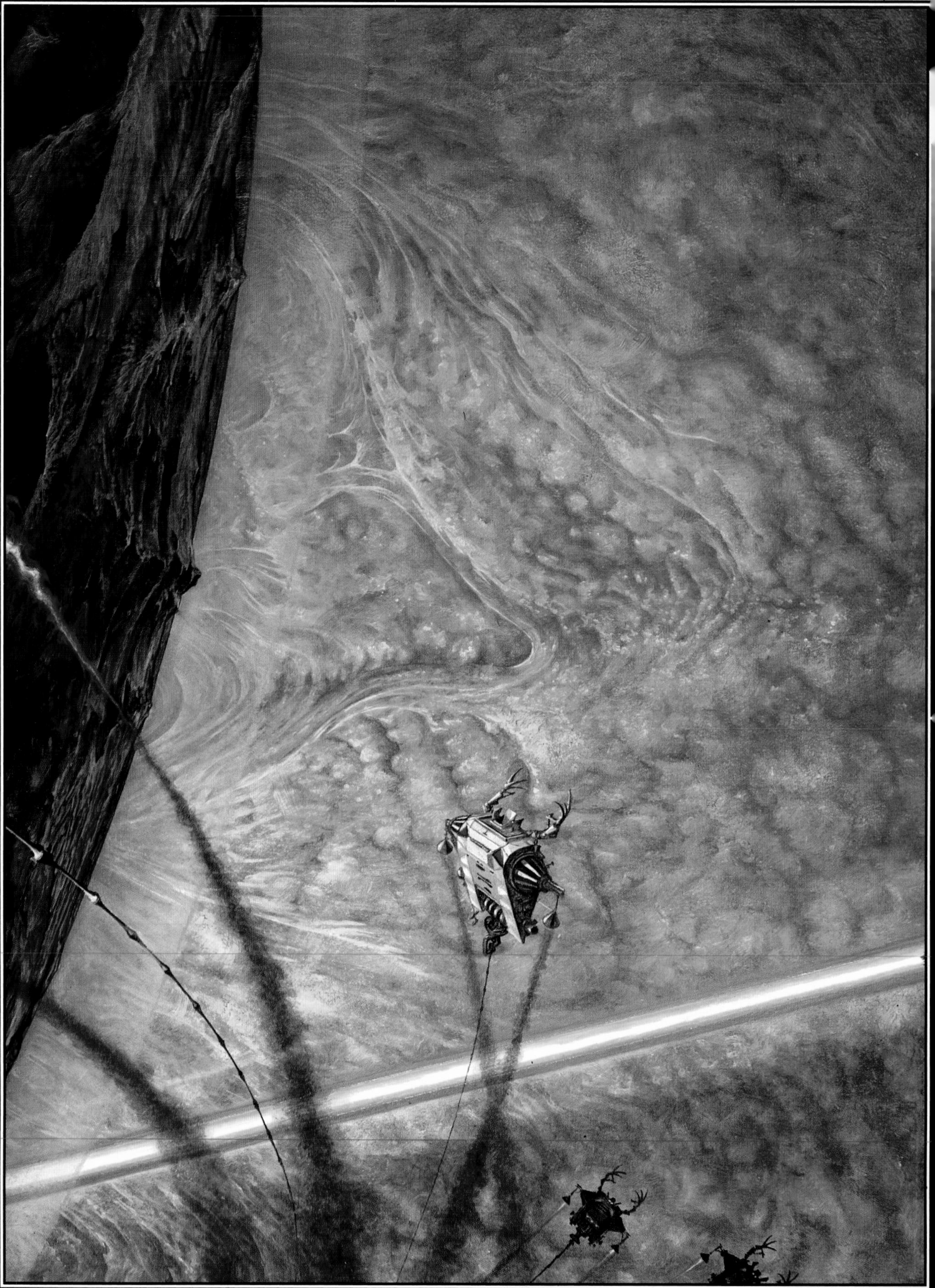

It was an enormously complex task to extricate *Hermes* from her decaying orbit around Saturn. Today the alien space-craft is safely installed in orbit above Titan Base.

In space a billion years shall pass like an afternoon. Five years are but the twinkling of an eye.

I must apologise for the way in which my writing style tends to adopt the quasi-biblical metaphor and simile so prevalent in the book. It seems impossible to deal in grandeur, without grandeur infecting even our words.

When we walk in a temple, shall not all our talk be in a temple whisper?

This problem of the decaying orbit obviously became the immediate priority. It required a huge flotilla of tugs, a delicate and vastly expensive exercise in spatial navigation, to extricate the vessel from its plight. Yet strangely small was its mass, though huge its bulk. Slowly, with infinite gentleness, it was tugged and coaxed, patiently manoeuvred into a new position, a stationary orbit, stable at least for the next two hundred years, immediately above Titan Base itself.

At U.N.T.W. Headquarters in New Tokyo the General Assembly was in special sitting. Uncharacteristically unanimous was the decision to dedicate unlimited funding, computing facilities, personnel allocations — indeed everything needed to investigate the vessel as soon as possible. As they well knew however, it would be many years before any in-depth studies could be established. Transport of men and machinery from distant Earth was slow and costly. For the time-being at least, the team already stationed on Titan Base must cope with the thing on their own, must make do with whatever expertise and equipment they could muster.

Hermes threw a huge shadow, slipping like a small eclipse across the Titan landscape. It might have been less alarming if the ship had looked less bizarre, more like a machine, less like a wild beast. As I already said, it was hard to believe it was not alive.

So the investigators of Project Hermes, amateur archaeologists seconded from other perhaps more hard-nosed disciplines, gradually pieced together the derelict's strange history. And as we all now know, this single vessel was nothing but the last tiny remnant of a huge fleet, only a small scout-ship, an exploratory craft, adaptable to the two modes of flight, both in outer space and in the atmospheres of planets. It seemed indeed that this was one of the very craft that had made landings on Earth itself. Others, it seemed, had been less fortunate, had destroyed themselves in sad catastrophes, vain attempts to establish a foothold on other, less suitable planets. Unmarked graves on unnamed worlds. How many failed we may never know, but of this we can be sure: only on the Second Earth did their long exile end. Only on our planet did they find a world as hospitable as the one they had lost. We now know, albeit at second hand, that though it sparkles with the promise of a box of priceless jewels, the universe is unutterably poor. And even this mighty super-civilization, combing its vast galleries for a new home, found in all the universe only two habitable worlds. One had been destroyed millennia before. The other was here. The other was Earth.

ABOVE: The so-called *archive* compartment contained an enormous wealth of information.

BELOW: The standard two-man "crab" tugs were invaluable shuttles from Titan Base to the orbiting alien.

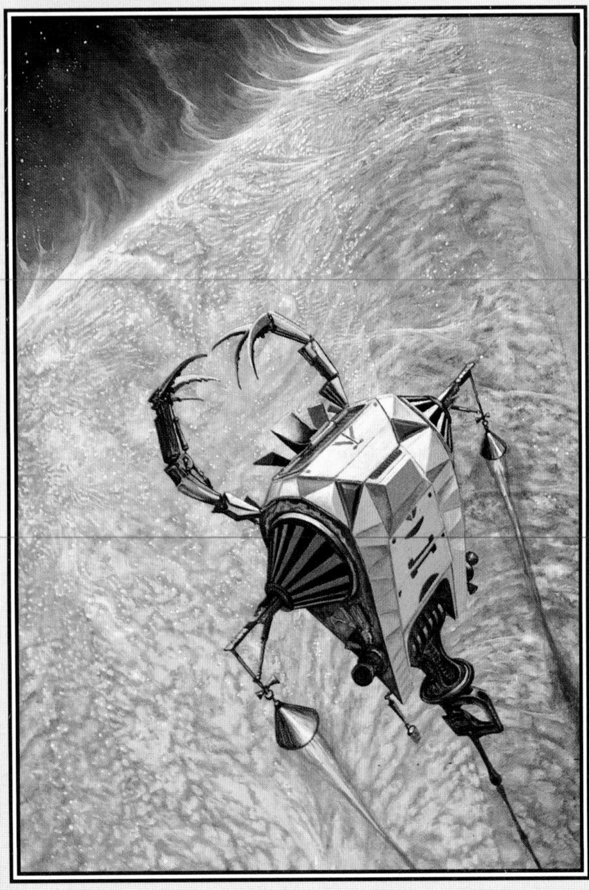

It was this sad fact that galvanized us all. And 2379 was a momentous year. The change seemed to come almost overnight. Goodbye to war, farewell to the politics of greed. Suddenly we were one world. For the Earth is our one and only home, a lonely life-raft tossing in an empty sea.

The so-called *archive* compartment offered the obvious entrance, for its doors yawned open. An invitation to the thief. Here all the riches were on display, on offer as it were to the casual passer-by. But there are precious few passers-by near Saturn's rings. As we now know, we were not unexpected visitors.

The library was vast, a circular dome one thousand yards in diameter, and the researchers, prosaic materialists to a man, scanned the endless compartments with uncharacteristic expressions of awe and wonder. This huge dome, crammed with knowledge, was just one tiny part of a tiny part, and the whole ship itself the mere tender of an even larger vessel. Then in turn the larger vessel was nothing more than the fragment of a fleet, a fleet so huge that it had crossed the millennia with an entire civilization. The race that built this library had lived in empty space for thousands of years, never breathing the fresh, pure air of a real world, their feet never touching a floor they had not built themselves. They had never known the taste of wild fruit, the smell of snow upon the mountain, the tang of flung spray at the water's edge. For them, all these things were legend, mythology, half-forgotten stories handed down from century to century. They had almost stopped believing. Until they found our planet, that is, and legend became history.

Until they found the Second Earth, and history began to re-write itself.

The archive will take years to fully understand. Perhaps some of its documents will never be deciphered. There are vast literatures in scores of languages, huge collections of scientific and historical records. There are catalogues, taxonomies, bestiaries of alien life-forms, endless sad lists of planets explored and rejected. There are musical

Hermes — or a craft of a similar type — lifts off from a landed mother-ship.

The tail-assembly was apparently used mainly for course corrections. Equipment is also housed here for taking samples of the atmospheres of planets.

works without number, symphonies, operas, oratorios, all imprisoned in pseudo-crystalline recording devices.

And in every case, though the languages vary, the voices are unmistakably, heart-wrenchingly human.

There are thousands of works of art too, paintings of the home-world, that far-off, long-dead sister of the Earth. There are ikons, portraits, images of their ancient divinities. And in every case, though the details vary, the features are undeniably human, and even their gods seem to have been created in the image of man.

But all this cultural treasury had to wait. The first investigators could unlock only the easier mysteries, decipher only the least cryptic messages. So this is where the ideograms fitted in. It seemed so neatly planned, as if the long-dead masters of Hermes had foreseen the accessibility of ideograms, even to minds untrained in the study of alien languages.

So the so-called PENTATEUCH — five books of ancient scripture pre-dating by many thousands of years our own Judaic *Pentateuch of Moses* — came to be the first text that yielded to the code-breakers. And of course it was in those five books, and also in the later so-called CODA, that the great message of Hermes was to be read. And what a surprise it was when we found that the message was directed — not at some unnamed posterity — but, like the pointing finger of a judge pronouncing sentence, at us ourselves. *We* are the heirs of that space-borne race. The message came direct from *our own ancestors.*

So here it is, re-published in a fuller glory, augmented from other parallel narratives, illustrated with visual material taken from the archive itself. And it must be emphasized here that this edition is not only a translation and a deciphering; it is also a consensus edition, based on the writings of many men, the visions of many artists.

All of whom were dead long before our own history began.

A NOTE ON THE IDEOGRAMS

Celia Hiroshige
Exo-linguistics New Tokyo

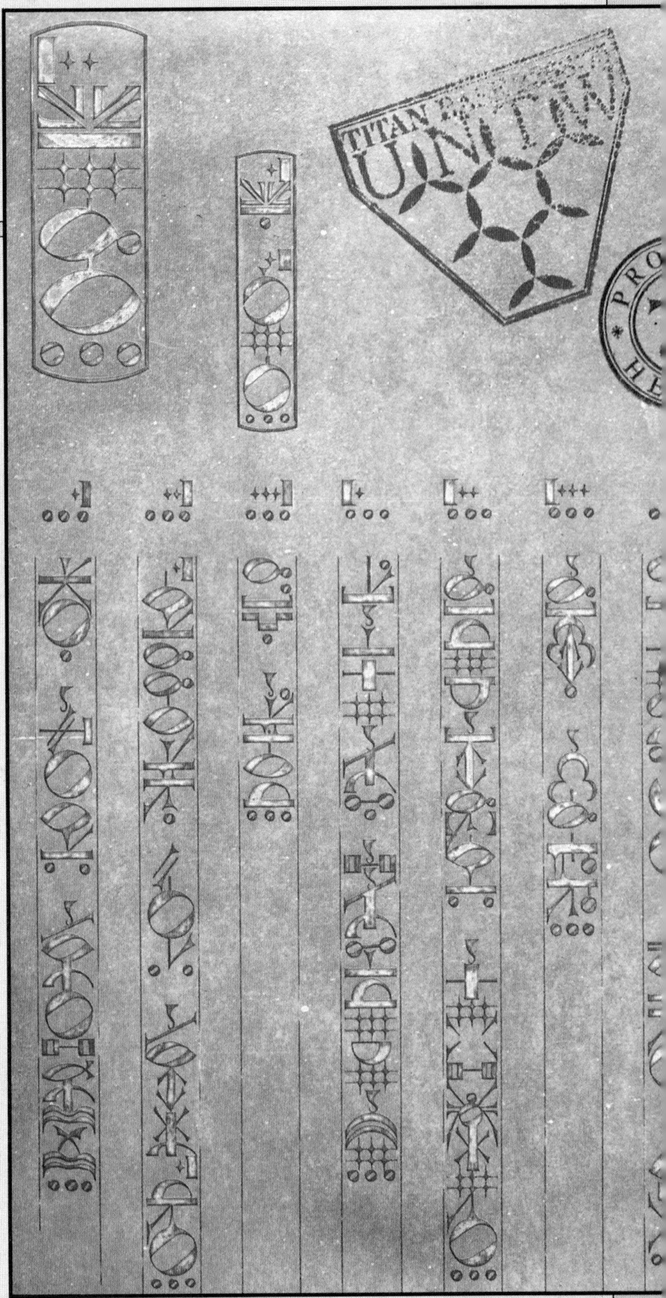

The first tablet of scripture to be deciphered. Originally engraved on copper, the message was electronically rendered in colour to provide enough contrast for "documatic" transmission to Earth.

In 2380 I wrote a short commentary on the *Hermes* ideograms for the first edition of PENTATEUCH. I also provided some footnotes to the text to explain the interpretation of several of the more interesting symbols.

Very little has emerged from subsequent research to make me change my interpretation very radically, though it must be admitted that the additional sources have certainly helped to extend our appreciation of the deliberately multi-faceted — sometimes indeed deliberately ambiguous — texts.

Apart from the obviously fuller narrative, there are very few respects in which this edition differs from that of 2380. The only important difference is more of an omission. The names of various divinities — *Verdrinn, Ildrinn* etc., even of certain creatures, the *Weedlekinn* for example — have been rendered this time not by spelling out the sound of the names as they are heard on recordings, but only by their accurate and purely ideographic identity — "the bride of Glass", "the forgotten bride of man" etc. The *Weedlekinn* however, represented ideographically as "mighty wanderers of the sea", we prefer to call simply "whales". We also follow a similar policy with the many names of *God,* translating whichever ideographic title seems contextually appropriate — "the fatherless child", "the child of the void" etc. We feel this to be justified on the grounds that this is somehow decidedly not the God of our own much later religions. This is a fallible God, forgetful, prone to bouts of sloth, negligence, even an uncomfortably anthropoid sexuality. Indeed whatever *religion* emerges from these pages would seem to present a deity by no means all-knowing, all-seeing, in control of his universe. This is not the Allmighty at all. On the contrary, he seems not even to be credited with *creation* as such; he is more the observer of some quasi-automatic process in which he is only the catalyst, and driven by needs, emotions and desires very much like those of mortal human beings. Fortunately, we no longer destroy such heresy by *auto da fe.*

Indeed the happy effects of this heresy have probably changed human civilization beyond recognition. Let us hope that the improvement will last.

Back to the ideograms.

To communicate with a total alien, a creature that understands neither our spoken nor our written language, it may be a good idea to resort to hand-signs or to drawings in the sand. Indeed, in all projects in the past whereby man has attempted to send messages to hypothetical intelligent races elsewhere in space, the need has always been recognized for a system of signs or ideograms, in which simple statements might be made in a form that transcended language.

If an alien race needed to understand all our literature without any cues or prompting from ourselves, then they might well discover ironically that the first texts to be deciphered would be the oldest — ancient heiroglyphic or pictographic inscriptions made long before the abstractions of our advanced culture made such communication impossible.

And so it was with the Hermes archive. Its masters knew this very well. The most prominently displayed "volume" at the entrance to the great archive was in fact — of all the literature contained there — the one work which carried almost the whole message in its most succinct and accessible form. Only the so-called CODA needed to be added, and the message was complete and unequivocal. The CODA, the only tablet to have been engraved or stamped from pure gold, was produced at more or less the same time that the spacecraft was abandoned. This has been thoroughly confirmed by modern dating procedures.

The masters of the Hermes simply updated their ancient scriptures in what was already to them a dead "language". They wanted to be sure that we, their own distant descendents, would get the whole story — right up to the date when, to quote Dr. Glover, *history began to re-write itself.*

It must be understood above all that the main source of this edition, the incised tablets of the PENTATEUCH OF THE COSMOGONY, is entirely ideographic, bearing no true relation to the spoken or written word. The tablets are not, strictly speaking, capable of being "read" in the usual sense of the word. They carry only a series of quasi-mystical symbols, each of which represents a "quantum" of philosophical concepts and attitudes already familiar to the individuals for whom the inscriptions were made. There were probably many interpretations of each statement, even — it has been suggested — deliberate ambiguities.

There is no distinction between the parts of speech to which we are accustomed — no verbs, nouns or adjectives. One symbol may have the function of all three, and a "statement" is made up simply by stringing separate characters together. This process is described in the appendix, where we also reproduce a very brief list of some common ideograms and the way in which they are put together.

Use of the ideograms was not confined to the tablets of scripture. Here the symbol for *darkness* is used on a war-plane, perhaps for purposes of identification.

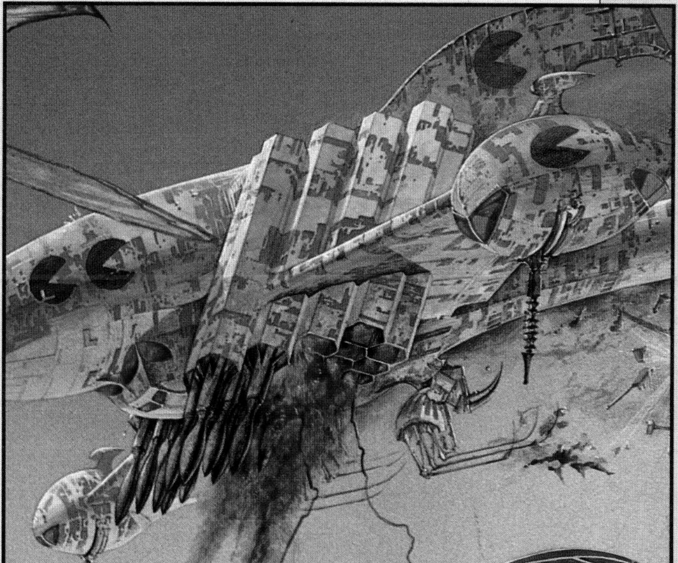

The five book-titles as they appear on the metal tablets. The final "cartouche" represents the ambiguous symbol *The end/The beginning.*

The text of the Pentateuch is, as its name indeed indicates, divisible into five very distinct books or sections. In the principle set of tablets, those deciphered in 2379, the sections were already of different length, but in this later edition Book Five (*The Last Things that were Made*) dominates the other four even more, being over eight times as long as Book Four.

This is simply because most of the additional material is, as one might expect, mainly concerned with the history of man. Furthermore, a large section is missing from most sources (see our Chapter 14), where at some time an expurgation of the account of man's origin has reduced the length of Book Four even more.

For this reason, and for reasons of design, we have decided to dispense with the five-fold division entirely, and to substitute instead a more fitting breakdown into thirty-one more or less equal chapters. The titles of these chapters are however far from arbitrary; all were used as *cartouche* headings at the appropriate points in one or other of the various sources.

The musical sub-headings also appear in several sources, though not necessarily all of them in every one, nor occurring in precisely the order we have used. The so-called CODA was of course added later, so we have given it the status of an epilogue rather than of a chapter.

When the king is asleep and the sailors aweigh
And green things come from the sea and play,

The bells shall wait for the ladling can
And time and tide for the weather man.

1 PRELUDE

THE FIRST EYE

Time and space. Being and non-being.
The child of the void, alone.

Things.

The first things.

A raindrop, a grain of sand, a bead of glass, a pebble?

They are here, they began. Somehow they were persuaded into being. Like fishes, like birds, they swim, they fly. How can this be? A pond contains the finny multitude, a sky the feathered host.

Yet all *was* dark. Had *always* been dark, *dark before it was dark*. Nothing stirred; neither saw nor spoke, neither thought nor felt. All was dead and seamless night, a shroud for the unborn. A coverlet for the yet-to-be.

Imagine it. Just think it through — *nothing* existed — anywhere. Only the lonely wheel of time, measure of nothing.

In that vast, unfathomed mystery an unseen clock began to tick, had ticked even before it *began* to tick. Space unfolded like a black sheet, a never-ending nothing spilling from a drawer. The closet never emptied, was never full. Space is silent, unseen, unheard, unknown; it is the business of the night, when every creature sleeps, every eye is closed.

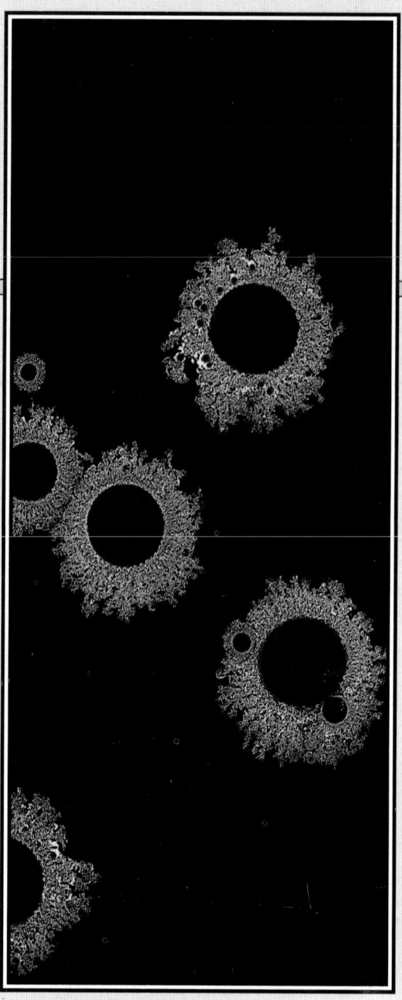

Curds in the void, squeezed from something less than the milk.

The clock ticks. The clock ticks.

The clock ticked even before it *began* to tick.

And yet the black is filled, embroidered with its fiery cities. How can this be?

Curds in the void, squeezed from something less than the milk. And all at once the vessel had a measure of its own emptiness, for it was perception itself that came first, not the things perceived. How else could it be?

An eye opened. Saw nothing. Closed.

The witness awaited his own deed.

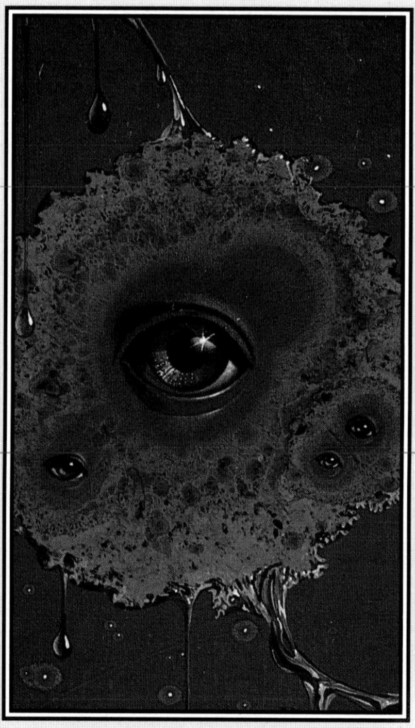

An eye opened. Saw nothing. Closed.

The eye opened. Saw nothing. Yet the eye was not blind.

An ear listened. Heard no one. Ached.

The father yearned for the cries of unborn children.

The void opened its huge beast-throat and bellowed. It yawned its unfocussed boredom, sighed its deep, deep loneliness, its aching sadness, the frustration of untried senses.

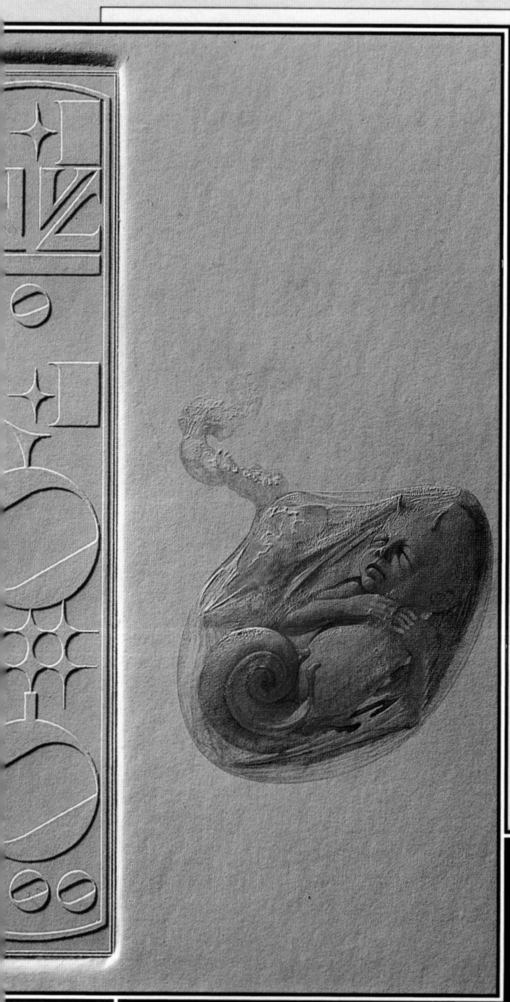

The witness awaited his own deed.

The sigh defined the soundless hollow, echoed, brought forth another sigh, another yawn.

The black draperies of time and space heaved and fluttered. A black storm, a black sky. Slow, black waves on a black beach, whispering softly in, whispering softly out. A black beast that breathed. The first child slept on the black beach.

Sleep was already ages old.

The eye opened. Saw nothing. Wept.

Impatience and sadness puckered the skin of darkness. The black sheet fluttered, making short-lived pockets of its own nothingness, turning its own nothingness inside-out, rhythmic, alternating bubbles of being and non-being. It was black linen hanging on the wind to dry, seeming to chatter as it flew: *I am... I am not... I am... I am not...* And by its very impatience to *be*, even the black void itself knows a tenuous, fleeting life.

The eye opened. Saw nothing. Closed.

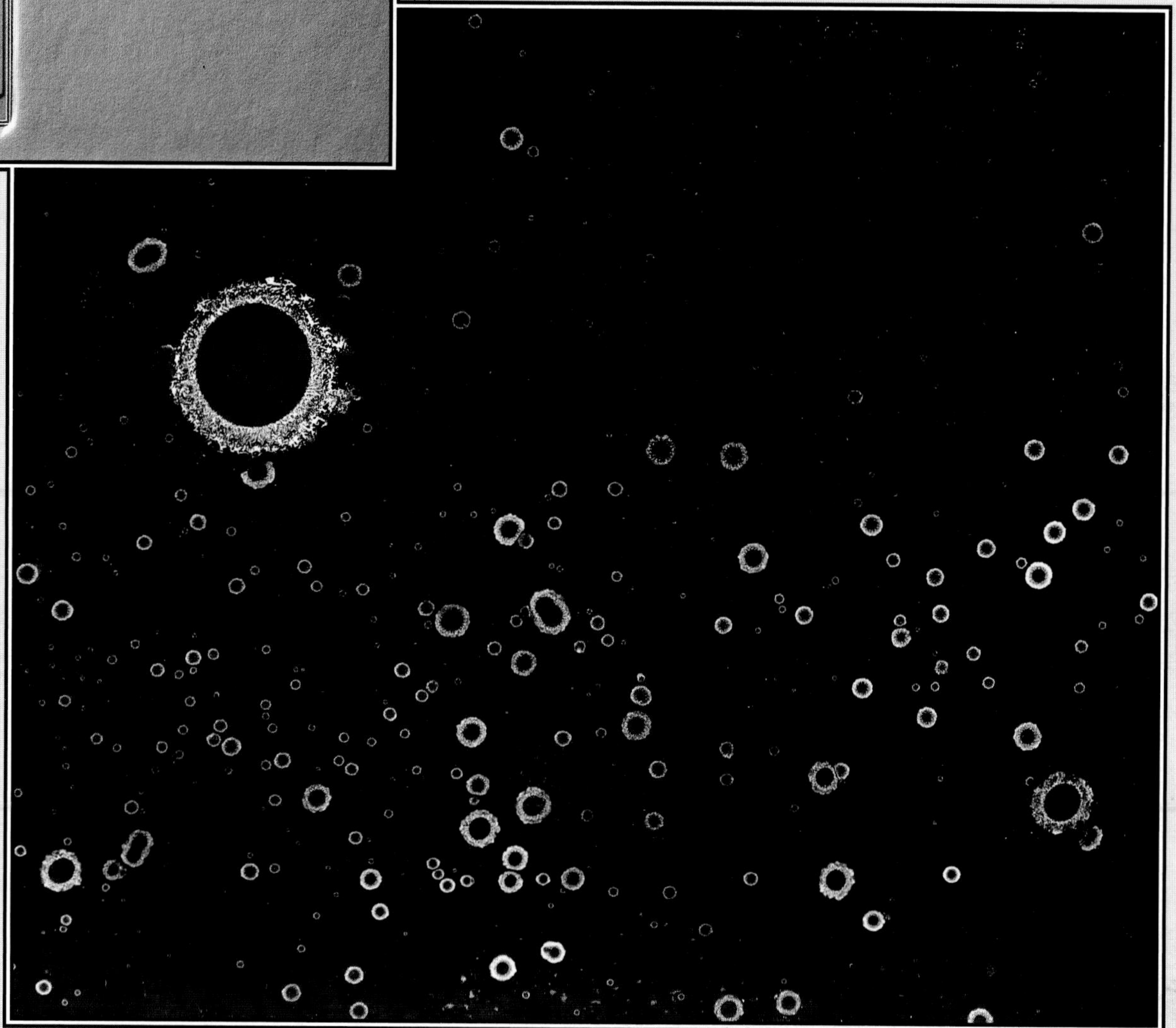

"The first fruits of the void."

2 OVERTURE

THE CHILD OF THE VOID

Dream and non-dream. Growth. Pain. The first light.

Dreams beyond the young understanding...

The sleeper became the dreamer. Dreams beyond the young understanding, images beyond imagination. Swimming. Sparkling wave-crests riven by the thrust of scaly limbs. Flying. Cool, glass-clear wind beaten by the rhythm of exultant wings.

Beautiful beasts tested their limbs in playful battle, their horns locked together in double spirals like loving snails. Smooth, delicate horns, prettily made, caressing, gripping the hard-curled dream-horns in a gentle embrace. And sound was in the dream-ear, the music of a consoling voice, feathery. Sweetly perfumed skin brushed the dream-cheek like a blessing.

Sleep was a warm nest, a womb suspended in the black void. A tiny hand flailed. Then, searching for some reality beyond the dream, it broke through the soft cocoon of sleep. It sought the hand of another, but found only the sleeper's other hand, touched only its tiny mirror-image in the dark. The hand was already ages old.

The eye opened. Saw no one. Wept.

The child of the void knew its own solitude. And shall any man, with mother, father, siblings and friends, ever plumb the depths of that loneliness, or gauge the sorrow of a *whole universe* without life? No blanket against the cold, no curtain to ward off the night, no gentle hand to soothe away the nightmare.

And the nightmare was real. The cradle was also the tomb. Death more terrible where there had never been life. Darkness thicker without so much as the memory of light. And cold has no frontiers where there was never warmth.

So even when the dreams grew weak and far between, the eye stayed firmly closed, waiting for escape to be renewed. The child whimpered fitfully, afraid of wakefulness, clinging to sleep through a long, long babyhood, dreaming away the unmeasurable ages.

Yet the clock still ticked unheard. Unseen, unknowable fingers pointed to the æons one by one and bade them pass away.

The sleeper grew; new, unbidden strength. The fingernails of the dead lengthen, even in the tomb. For the pendulum swings, the sweep-hand sweeps, and even the child of the void cannot derail the unstoppable mechanics of time.

Stronger, cleverer, wiser he grew, as all things must; yet also sadder, more aware of his own grief. And the dreams gave shorter and duller refuge, ever more ghostly consolation. So the curtains parted, self-pity yielding to wrath, ill-defined sorrow to a burning, screaming pain.

Two eyes opened. Saw nothing. Yet remained angrily open.

Then the child, his mouth hitherto but the fountain of sobs and keenings, roared like a brass bull, like thunder, like storm, like bellows-fire. One imprisoned soul yearned for a mother it had never had, called to unborn brothers and sisters lost or astray in the mindless heavens, pleaded for an unimagined lamp to dispel the thick darkness of its cradle, its tomb.

So the curtains parted, self-pity yielding to wrath...

The pain in the head burned like a yellow sword, warmed him somehow in the reflection of his own hot anger. His hands rubbed at his eyes to dispel the itch. Then slowly the sobbing subsided, as sobbing always will in time. Tears fell unseen from his eyes and from his fingers, a warm, salt wetness. He tasted the salt on his lips, was reminded again of his grief. But now the surge redoubled like the wave that meets its elder brother returning from the cliff.

And the yellow sword grew in his head, a blade of razor-sharp grief, cutting itself free, piercing the very walls of his being.

Then suddenly, like a cross of gold, the first light, the first star was hanging before him in the black void, its lovely brightness reflected in every tiny tear that the child had shed.

And so there was light, though no eye had yet seen it. And there was first colour — red and blue and yellow — for the light reached out to the edge of the void, where the great disc of time slowly turned like a coloured wheel.

Silence, no more grief, no more loneliness. The universe held its breath, waiting for the child to open its eyes.

The first deed awaited the first witness.

The clock ticked. The wheel turned.
Light was already ages old.

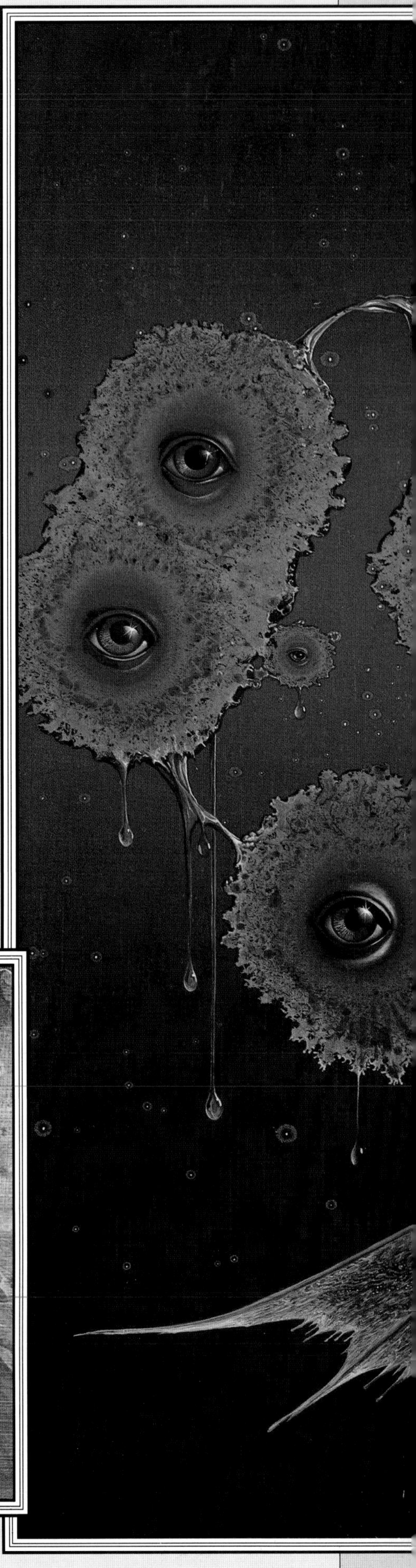

And so there was light, though no eye had yet seen it.

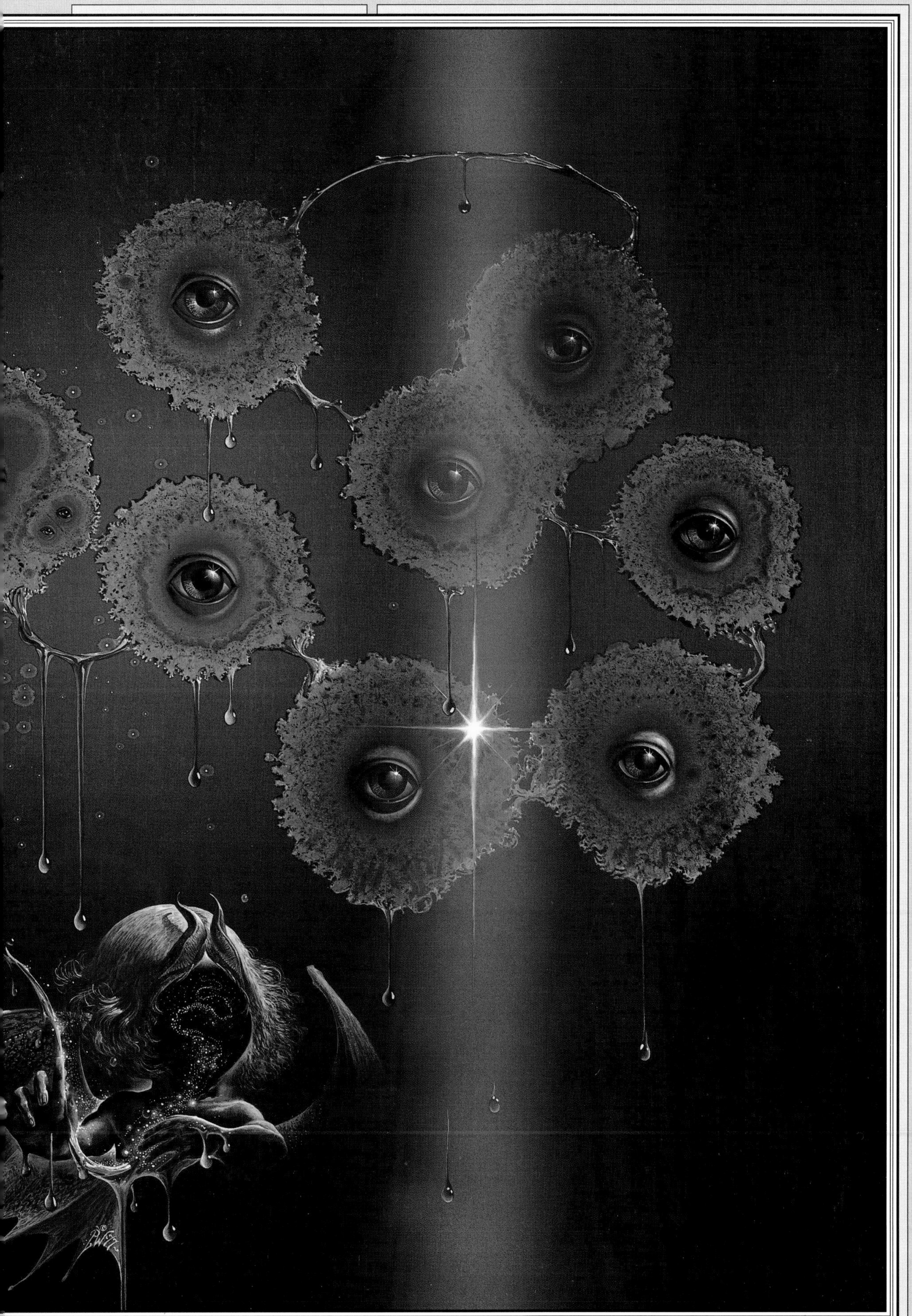

3 SOLO

THE FIRST HEAVEN

Sleeping and waking. The stars live and die.

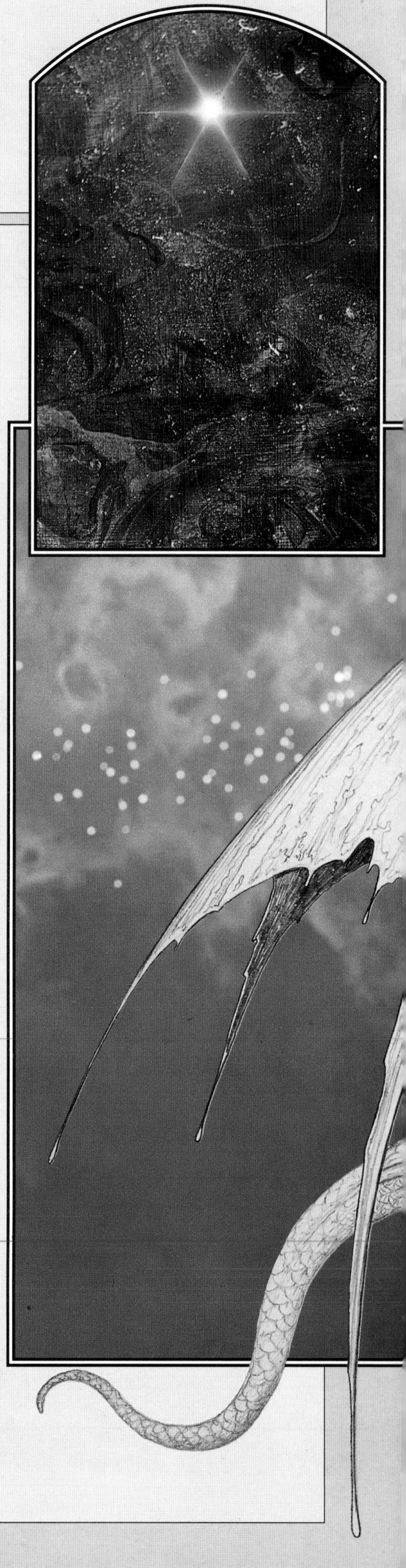

An eye opened. Saw. Stayed open, tears drying away.

A bright, painted merry-go-round turned. At its centre stood the great yellow sword, the echo always answering the cry, the need somehow fulfilled by its own expression, the event mysteriously prompted by its own observer.

The sleeper looked around him, the watery wounds of his eyes somehow staunched by vision itself. He smiled, he laughed. In every teardrop were tiny images of himself, distorted grins, bulbous, chuckling faces.

Light, sound, joy. Creation had begun.

So the child broke free from the cocoon of sleep, sloughed it off like a snake its dried skin, too small a vessel for such swelling joy. Horns he had like a crown, and wings like a royal mantle, and a tail scaled like overlapping coins of gold. He took the yellow sword in his hands for a sceptre, stood upon the very axle of time. Proclaimed himself king.

Light, sound, joy. Creation had begun.

Yet such a new king needed no throne, unfitted for sitting, too full of vigour not to fly, not to swim. Like a joyful bird he flew to the edges of the void, where time's great rainbow slowly turned. He sped along the coloured rim, scattering light and colour as he went, each joyful thought, each peal of laughter somehow manifest in lasting form. A host of twinkling stars followed him through space in a happy cavalcade.

The great wheel turned, blue, yellow and red. Colour everywhere. The blackness of the void was dispelled. A billion tiny lamps, strings of brightly-shining beads, garlands of warm flowers. He braided them one to another in wreaths and posies, circlets, bouquets, nosegays... flinging them off into every empty place. Even the tiniest star chattered to itself like a baby. The vault of Heaven, once a blank and silent tomb, was filled with shouting and singing, a children's playground loud with a strange and noisy chase. Catch as catch can. Blind man's buff. The games were already ages old.

And the play-master slowed, tired by the chase, exhausted by joy. He turned, he toppled, he rolled. Then, abandoning his body to its own momentum, folding himself up in his wings, he went to sleep. The king became the sleeper, then the sleeper once more the dreamer. But this was a new kind of sleep, a new kind of dream. Not a place to hide, but a place to rest. Not the closing of a door, but the promise of a million doors to open.

Horns he had like a crown, and wings like a royal mantle, and a tail scaled like overlapping coins of gold.

A shadow passed over the smile, darkening the soft cheek like a storm-cloud on a Summer meadow.

Like a round stone on a river-bed he rolled gently along the wheel of time, his dream-eye somehow glancing across it, seeing fleeting glimpses of all the things he would do. Short-cuts æons long.

Wonder. Mystery. A gilded patch-work of love and joy. Yet somehow there was also a tincture of sadness, a sadness that seemed strangely unfixed, embedded in half-remembered futures in between. There was a face — not his own image, but a *new* face — pressed tenderly close to his, with tiny horns upon its brow, now curled liked pretty shells, now sharp and cruel like curved swords. Then crimson blood stained the deadly points. A shadow passed over the smile, darkening the soft cheek like a storm-cloud on a Summer meadow. But then the shadow would pass, and the smile return. Beautiful, comforting, warm, yet somehow tainted by the sharp memory of menace, pain and anger.

Like a blind man in an unfamiliar room, the sleeper sought extra detail, reached out with his dream-arms, his dream-fingers spread. Smooth skin upon his cheek, gentle breath in his ear. Suddenly a warm body pressed against him in the darkness. Perfumed hair. A wild joy, unguessed promise, tenderness, a thrill of pleasure.

And so he slept on, dreaming mystery upon mystery. Yet still alone. The clock ticked away the unrecorded centuries, meaningless history, unmade, unwritten. And still he grew, matured by dream-life, his strength increasing unawares like wine fermenting in a great vat of sleep.

Sweet was the dream, with white sand sea-shore and cliff-tops carpeted with soft turf.

And where was man? And where the Earth? The sleeper dreamed, and all his creatures stood upon his awakening, courtiers around the bed of the king, waiting for life to be shared out, distributed like a boon. But could it be that time could be forgot, and all our futures never be, for want only of a cosmic cock to crow?

Sweet was the dream, with flower-broidered mead and drowsy pleasure-garden. A dream of perfumed breath made history wait; the scribe pauses, holds his breath, his pen half-way to paper, suspended...

Sweet was the dream, with white sand sea-shore and cliff-tops carpeted with soft turf. A dream of Summer love made the universe shrink; the great wheel grows dim, slows like a mill-wheel in a drought...

Sweet was the dream, but the lights of Heaven flickered and faded like dying flowers. The stars wandered off like spiderlings and were lost in the depths of the void. Then darkness crept back, a black shroud. Silence fell, a leaden rug.

The last star winked out like a spent candle.
The dream was already ages old.

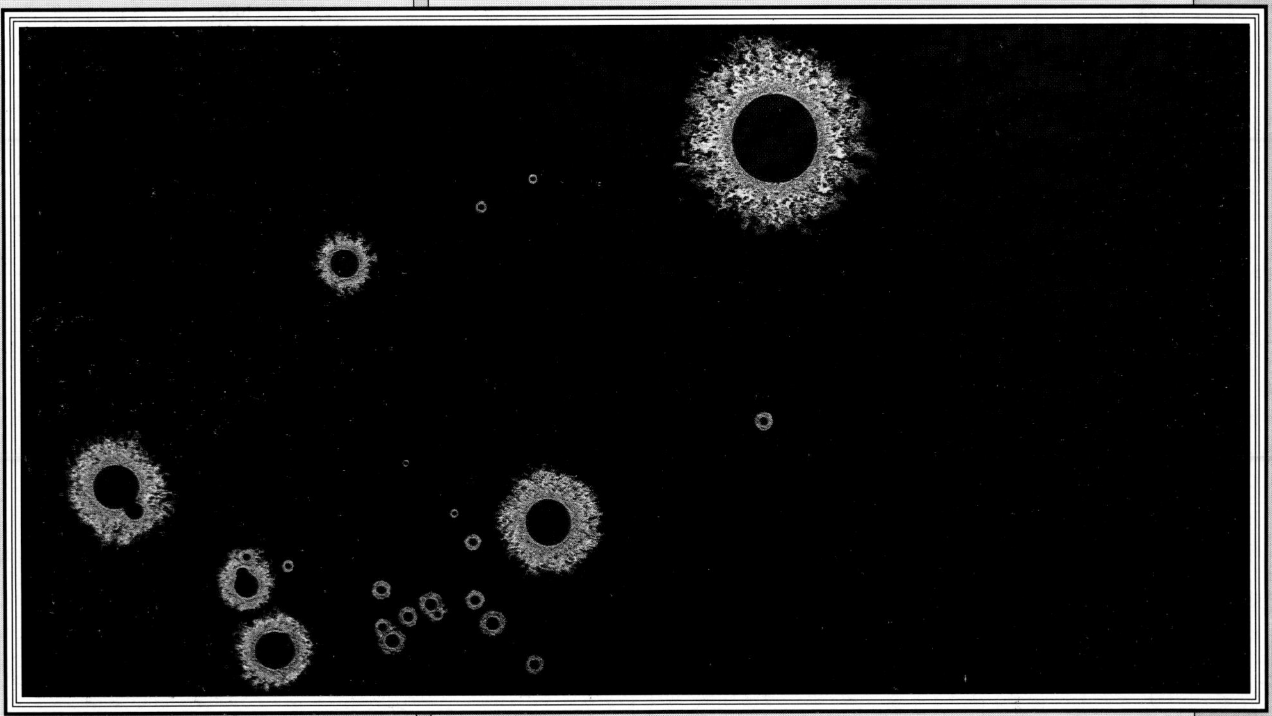

4 REPRISE

THE SECOND HEAVEN

Re-awakening. Guilt.

The dream flowed on. Green pasture, cattle, flower-filled forests. Oceans boiled with enamelled and jewelled fishes. Vision fermented in his brain, stronger, sweeter, like ale.

One dream-thing made another dream-thing, replica of itself, yet changing of its own accord. The dream flowed into differently shaped vessels, fitting itself to circumstance, yet remaining the dream, in the head, not in the flesh. Clockwork toys turned their own keys.

But the dream began to change. Now less of a plan. More a memory of the future. And once more that strange sadness, oddly linked with pleasures of the soft skin, the warm breath, the velvet whispering in the ear. Then the tenderness would withdraw. Sudden as a cloud. Cold as shadows on snow. He would dream a shout and a scream, not from his own throat; then anger, bitterness, sobbing accusation. To escape the shout, he flew from the dream like a startled bird.

He awoke.

The stars were dead. The wheel of time was black. Space crushed him like black feathers. Darkness shuttered his eyes, thick as black wool.

And all the unborn children waited for the king. And none cried *shame! neglect!* And no crier walked the city to call out: *Oyez! Oyez! The king awakes!*

Then light sprang from his horns again like a knife. Pain, loneliness, and now a new feeling. Guilt. Lonely as a lost child, guilty as a father, he gazed sadly at his own reflection in time's mirror, where space turns in and looks upon itself, an eye for an eye. And wept.

And many a man may look at a glass and cry: *I am old! What shall become of me?* But a man is not alone in his old age, and whatever becomes of him, his children and his friends shall bear his body to the hill, cast garlands on his bed and wish him well.

The motherless child looked in the mirror and wept. The childless father struck the mirror with the tip of his horn, leapt upon the wheel, touched it again with rainbow light. And the wheel continued to spin, groaning like a grind-stone, sparkling with knives. He flew along the rim, as he had when he first awoke, filling the heavens with garlands of light, blazing the dark pathways with lamps of flame. And each had a name and a mark, tethered to his memory by a chain of gold.

Stay awake. Determine. Resolve. Bring the dream to life. Learn the long story.

And therefore the First Earth, and man, and every beautiful thing that ever breathed.

And each had a name and a mark, tethered to his memory by a chain of gold.

5 RONDO

THE FIRST EARTH

The Earth and her Seven Moons. The Sun, the air and the sea.

The Earth was not a star. It gave no light at all. A dull earthenware pot hung among vessels of gold and silver, reflecting only the splendour of others. Yet, no less than all other made things, the Earth was a flickering thing, only a pulse of *yes* and *no*, *I am... I am not*. The clay was a language, a speech, a calculation. The whole sum encoded in but two digits, one and zero, *I am... I am not*. But still the clay had no form, the code-words unarranged. The clay awaited the potter. The words hung impatiently on the tip of the pen. History was about to begin.

And so he set to.

He rolled the clay into a ball and flung it out among the stars. It turned, it wandered, half-way between darkness and light, grey, the colour of dull zinc. Then seven others he set around it in a ring, bound to it by coloured tethers, ribbons of memory, chains of gold. Three moons for the first colours in the sky, blue and yellow and red. Three more for the colours in between, violet and green and orange. And last of all, a single lonely moon, black as coal, dull as lead, a dark reminder of something better forgot.

Why this? Why that? Did some deliberate thought guide the potter's hand? No thought but the stray fancy, the whim, the half-remembered dream, the half-seen future glimpsed across the wheel of time. The future waited to be made. Balls of clay queued up along the potter's bench.

A special star, a silver ball of pure white light hung nearby. The white ox waited for the wreath of flowers, waited to be chosen for the maying. And all the golden chains were buckled to her yoke. She was guardian, mother, leader of the herd.

The Earth swam. A fish on a line. And in a ring her coloured moons danced in time with the wheel of time, violet, blue, green, yellow, orange and red. All but one. The black moon, which men would one day call Darkness, hung motionless behind the Earth, hiding in that place of perpetual eclipse.

Sleep no more, said the black moon to the hand that made it, *lest darkness be the lot of all*.

The black moon stood in the shadow like a creature of the night.

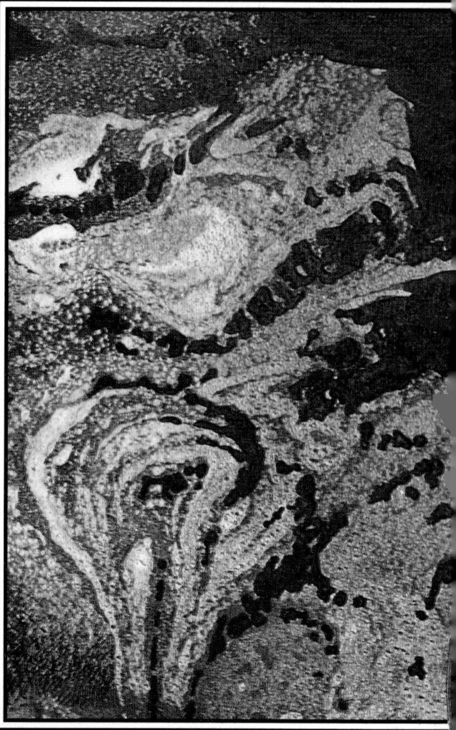

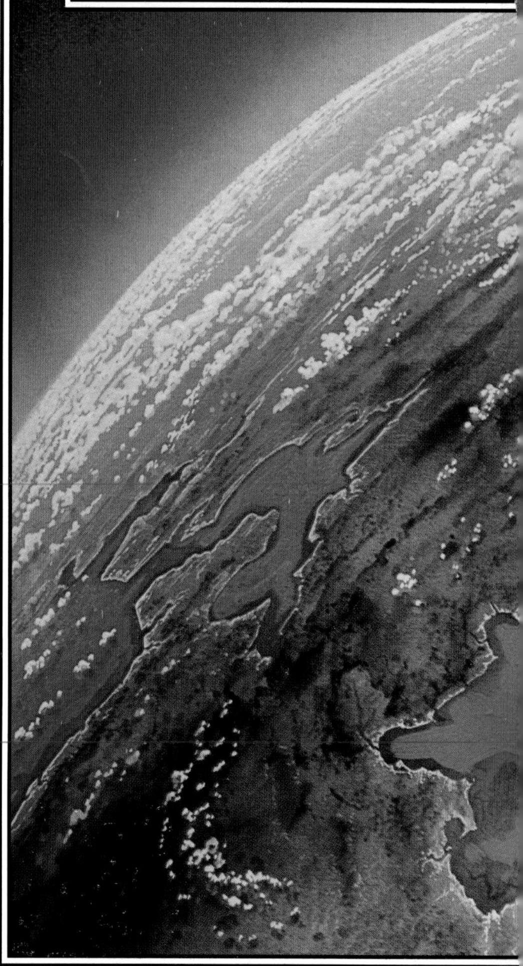

And therefore the First Earth and man, and every beautiful thing that ever breathed.

The clay worlds had no mark upon them but the unconsidered finger-print, random, undesigned. The sea waited in the dream. The mountains slept undiscovered in the sky. Unborn fathers attended the motherless child.

The white sunlight warmed the grey Earth-clay. The coloured moons rose and fell, crossing and re-crossing the empty ground. Strange, unwritten loyalties, invisible bonds. And the black moon stood in the shadow like a creature of the night. *Sleep no more*, said the black moon.

Then the clay yielded its water, reflecting the glory of the Sun. The Earth was ocean from end to end. The coloured moons gazed at their own young faces in the pool, a flawless sphere of mirror-polished zinc. The Earth was the stage, the moons for the time-being only spectators. But never doubt that the action would one day spill from the arch into the auditorium. Each moon would also have its play, comedy, history, tragedy.

The pen was dipped. The black ink hung on the sharpened quill.

Write, said the dark ink, *lest darkness be the lot of all.*

Never once did he pause for second thought, for second thought may flatten lyric into prose, bring down the dream-castle to the level of the cottage and the barn. Like a magic spell the dream spilled from his head.

And a new trick he learned. To mould the clay without so much as the touch of his hand. To write the play without the paper or the pen. The very thought was tool enough, sufficient in itself. So his last finger-prints, submerged in the great Earth-sea, were washed away like sand-ripples by the tide.

These are the things that he made. The first living things that were not him, the first children of the fatherless child.

But first, as he searched in the memory of the dream, all that came forth upon the Earth was sweet warmth and perfume, the memory of soft breath upon his skin. And so it came about that the Earth was made of air and water, though nothing stirred above nor below. No bellows to make a wind. No wind to move the sea. The Earth was silent and still.

6 CARILLON

BELTEMPEST

A governor for the air. First sounds. Storms and rain.

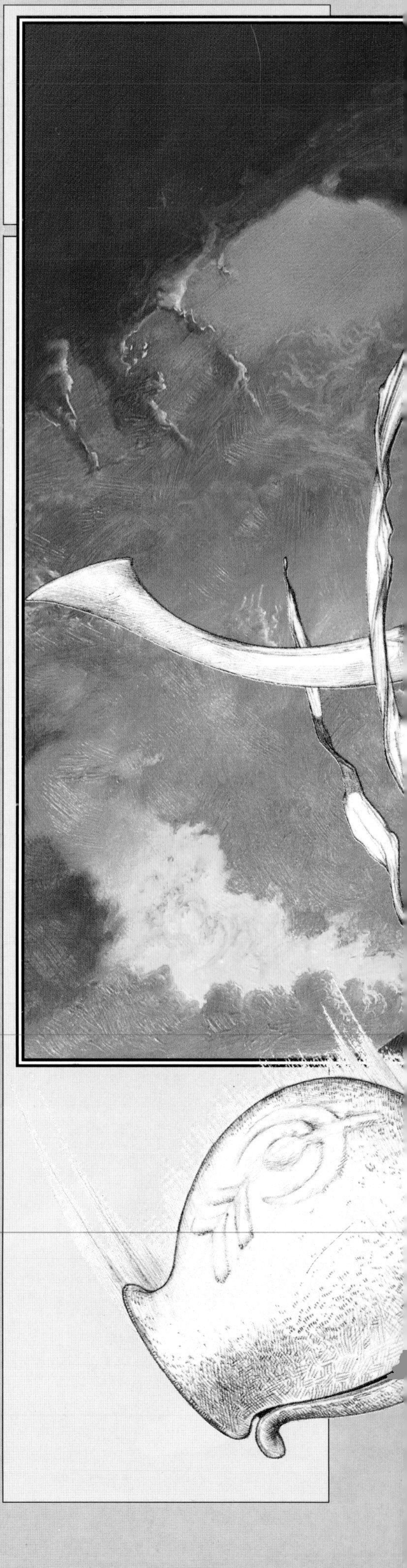

The dream came down to the sea like a wild beast. No longer a dream. The vault of the sky was filled by its white hair, shifting, changing shape, forming and re-forming. Like the roots of the mighty forest oak, its feet sank deep into the ocean floor. Like a mountain peak its broad, hairy back reared up into the sky. It had horns like monstrous trees. Golden eyes like beads of glass.

A new pair of eyes.

The child of the void was no longer alone. He gazed into the new eyes. The new eyes blazed back. Burning windows opened into another mind. Lightning flickered, jumping from one mind to the other, scribbling between Heaven and Earth. The air was damp, crackling with blue fire. *Make me an ear*, said the fatherless child, *that the guardian of the air may listen to his master.*

You are my first brother and my first friend. You are the first living thing in all the Earth. Your name is the first name: bell and storm. You may never be still. Your shape is obedient like the clay; fit it to the measure of our need. You shall never rest. Beltempest, sleep no more.

And the storm strode away, wading through the ocean like a wandering mountain. The water fell from his giant thighs in white cataracts, waves buckled before him like a rumpled carpet. Then, testing the obedience of shape, he sprang from the sea like an antelope, suddenly light and quick on his limbs. He raced. He flew. His hooves never struck the waves. And again, as if to try his talent, he grew suddenly huge and ponderous once more, crashing into the ocean like a fallen tree. The water sprang up where he fell, a silver crown sparkled round him, tumbled slowly back like rain.

Be glad, said his master. *The air and the sea must never die.*

Beltempest gazed upon his maker, his golden eyes burning with their own inner light. With a mute smile he pledged his dumb obedience, happy resolve. He would do as he was bidden, yet could answer neither by word nor wordless noise, for even now the Earth was still and

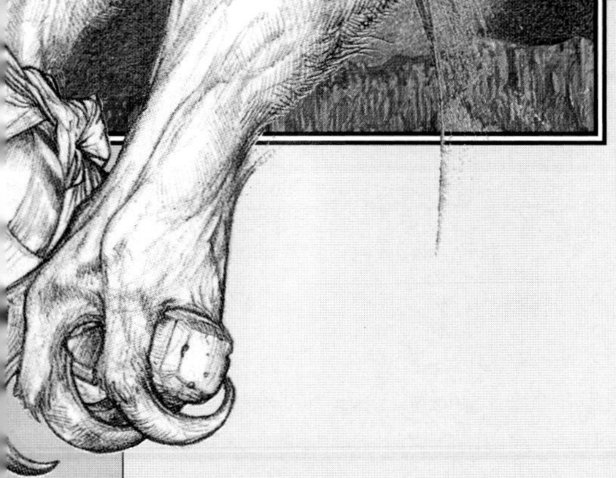

"You are the shepherd of the clouds," he said, "and with this bell you shall call them up."

had no voice.

I shall cure your dumbness here and now, said the child of the void. *My first friend shall speak*.

And on Beltempest's chin he placed the first trumpet, sudden-grown like a chanterelle. It brayed deeper, louder by the hour. Then in his mouth he planted the first tongue, the first voice, the first song. The trumpet was the storm, the song was the wind. Sound was like a living thing, and even the lifeless water stirred.

Joy. A new heart swollen with a nameless wonder. The horn blared. The song went round the Earth, a glad message from pole to pole. Noise, wondrous, wordless joy. The waves heaved up like listening hills, tumbled back like deafened valleys. Seething foam followed in a marbled train, braided with silver threads.

Beltempest strode the Earth.

Stand, said his master. And the governor of the air took from his master's hand a great dream-bell of brass.

You are the shepherd of the clouds, he said, *and with this bell you shall call them up.*

So the great bell chimed, summoned the clouds from the sea. Beltempest roamed with his flocks in the pastures of the sky, where a sign stood over the setting Sun, and the sign was this: that the first moon and the sixth moon should stand one atop the other as the light shall fall. The bow shall be the bell wall, the Sun shall be the clapper. This sign shall mean great tides, when all the flocks of Heaven hurry on the hills to pastures new.

The storm, the wind, the bleating clouds. *Your kingdom rings from end to end with noise. Beltempest, sleep no more.*

But at that time, when the whole Earth was new, every sound was but the echo of Beltempest's own doings. Proud as the squid, mightier than the whale, alone he strode the lonely Earth, where the mindless sea and the mindless sky copied his every move, subjects too obedient for a king who needed peers. No broken wave was there, neither trace of defiant cliff nor stubborn rock; the great waves rolled and rolled unhindered. Clear round the globe. At night, when the Sun hid behind the belly of the Earth... when only the dark moon walked the sky, betrayed by a black disc of missing stars... even in the darkest hour he did not sleep.

And no companion had he in the lonely watch.

The sea boiled. He was a ram. He was an army of rams. An army without anger, waging mock warfare with himself. A child in solitary play, speaking every part himself, villain, hero, hero's friend. There was neither land nor ship. Power unresisted, danger unchallenged. The grandeur was harmless. The spectacle unseen.

And the air and the water wed, spawning the rain, breaking the light in three. Three for the colours of the wheel of time, three for the colours of the bell of brass, three for the daughters yet to be.

Beltempest, you are guardian of all the air, and also of the place where air and water meet. Beltempest, sleep no more.

This sign shall mean great tides, when all the flocks of Heaven hurry on the hills to pastures new.

7 FANFARE

GLASS

A governor for the sea. The house of Glass. The music of the sea.

Below the waves, below the place where air and water meet, nothing but a green sameness. Nothing moved, nothing lived, nothing grew. The sea waited for the sea-dream.

And the dreamer visited Beltempest, climbed down through the sky on his great dragon's wings, shrank to the size of a tiny child, fluttered like a dove, settled a moment upon his very horn. No word, no understanding. How had a child made a giant from clay? And why did the giant weep?

Then the wings were suddenly furled, and plummet-fast he plunged to the ocean floor, where greenish semi-darkness settled round him like the primal void. And the dream spilled from his head.

The green draperies of the ocean heaved and fluttered. A green storm, a green sky. Slow, green waves on a green beach, whispering softly in, whispering softly out. A green beast that breathed. The second child slept on the green beach, in the arms of the fatherless child.

He was like a crystal, clear as air, his tiny body seeming nothing more than a trick of the light, optical sleight of hand.

Make me an ear, said the fatherless child, *that the guardian of the deep may listen to his master.*

You are my second brother and my second friend. Your name is only the second name in all the Earth. Your name is Glass, clear and pure. You shall keep this ocean for your own kingdom, yet always in trust for me. As I must look to the stars, and Beltempest your brother to his sheep, so shall you be warden of this place, and the husbandry of the sea shall be your task forever.

That the Glass should not cloud, nor the ocean die.

And they stayed at the bottom of the sea, fatherless child and childless father, sharing the dream of the family yet to be, sharing half-memories of fish, the whale-stories, the legends of the floating kingdoms, the unwritten history of the great Dry Land itself. Yet Glass was saddened by the sea. He was lonely, impatient for the dream to be a dream no longer. But in his head was no hint of how such things might come to pass.

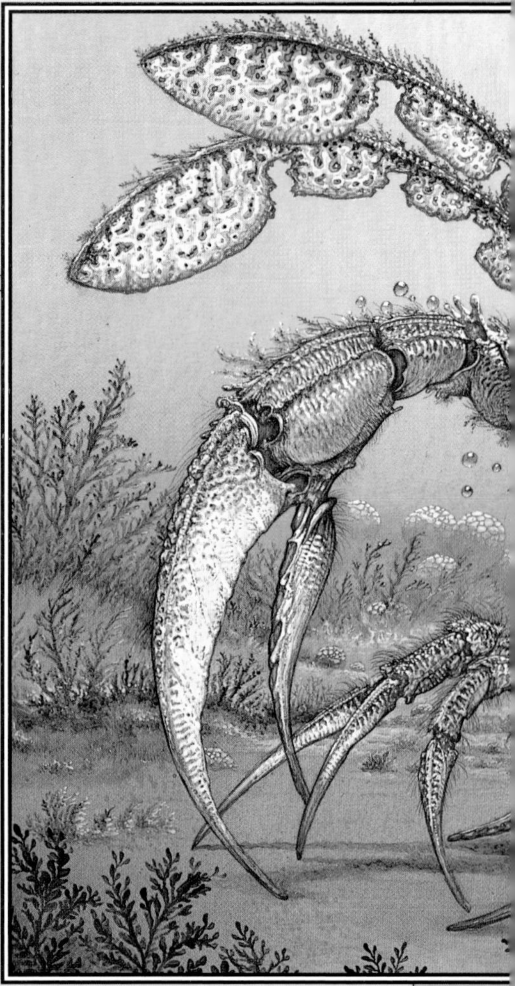

The sea waited for the sea-dream.

The palace built itself around him unawares...

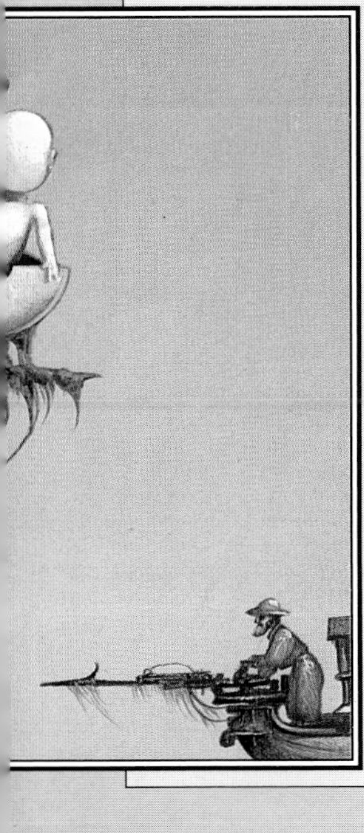

The clock ticked. The great wheel turned.

And yet the sea was filled, was peopled with a billion fish. How can this be?

And Glass was left alone, naked and cold.

His master watched, the easy cure for sadness in his own hand, waiting for some half-remembered miracle. The first stars had been his own pain. Perhaps by pain alone would come the first fish, a hot razor in the eye, a flame in the lonely mind, a golden blade suddenly swimming in the green? But Glass went away and hid. No word. No understanding. His master made the Sun itself, but cold was all around, and why did his master only watch him freeze?

So Glass hid himself in a deep darkness, with closed eyes and a closed heart.

And the cold built a palace in his mind. When he thought of a warm room, a soft refuge from the empty ocean, the palace built itself around him unawares... real, with walls of hard stone, and lined with polished pearl. No window. No door. A warm prison.

Yet here was the paradox: that his prison should set him free.

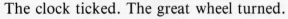

For here was a made thing, a miracle, and Glass alone had made it, his need leaking from the dream-world, clothing itself in stone. His master only watched, pleased that things should be made that were not made by him.

So Glass cut himself a door. Only the thought for his tool. Then bore the house upon his back, a wall and a roof of fluted stone, light as tomorrow's care, and his mantle was hemmed with purple jewels.

Then the child of the void was glad in his heart, overcome by unnamed love. Neither mother nor father had he, yet brothers he could make for himself, and his brothers should be the fathers of all the children of the Earth.

I set three horns upon your palace roof, he said, *that Glass may speak — to his master, to his brother, and to all his children yet to be.*

The water trembled as if alive, quivered with promise.

Each as perfect as a turnéd vase, singing as they grew, the three horns were made, quick as mushrooms. And their music burst forth, spreading through the empty ocean like a quickening shock. The water trembled as if alive, quivered with promise. And so the great diapason sounded, the joyful sea-song filling the cupped ear to its eternal brim. Both above and below the meeting-place of air and water, warmth, noise, endless song till the latter days.

That the Glass should not cloud, nor the ocean die.

And that is how the world began. Not easy.

The pen paused again, waiting for time to feed the word.

The memory of the dream was weak, must be rescued from dark places in the mind, must be brought to the light, cherished and tethered like a straying child. He dared not dream again, dared not even rest, for the universe lived only by his open eye, and all the stars hung only on his thread.

The pen paused. Memory faltered. The day-dream was a river. The nevous swimmer stood in the shallows, afraid of the current.

The air stood still to listen, and the waves fell. The horn, the bell and the tongue were dumb, and even the bleating clouds strayed back into the sea. Beltempest the giant, puzzled by a buzzing in the brain, waited for time to move the pen. And even in the sea the three horns were still, waiting for time to feed the word.

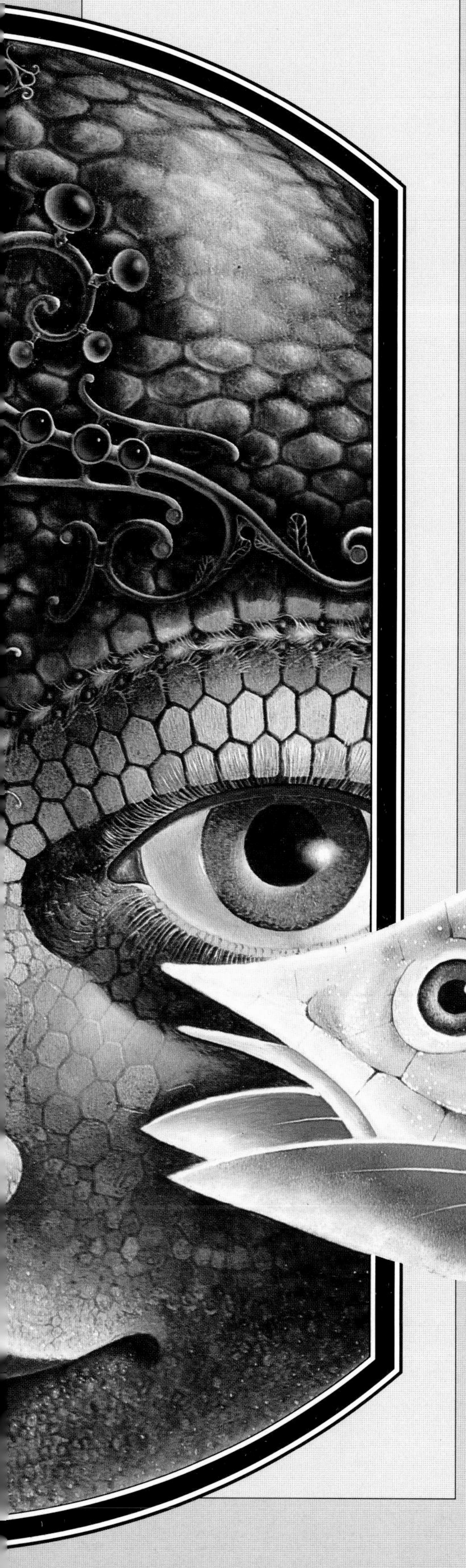

8 BALLAD

THE NYMPH-DREAM

Fantasy. Male dreams female.

A hornéd satyr chases a hornéd nymph, finds her in a hollow tree. Soft skin reflects skin-warmth. What arms are these that make this thrilling prison? What limbs that make such tender bars?

Only the dream, for no nymph had ever lived.

Dream-satyr chases dream-nymph. A mockery of a chase, so ready is the victim for the tender sacrifice. What prey is this that shares its cradle with the hunter? What beast is this that makes an infant of a king?

Only the dream, for no nymph had ever lived.

And the nymph-dream was shared among the brothers.

Beltempest left his throne in the sky, shrivelled to the stature of a mortal man. He lay upon the water like a ship-wrecked sailor, the waves lapping over him, dream-coverlet, dream-hair, dream-skin. Delirium. Confusion. Enchantment.

And Glass came forth from his house, lay on the sea-bed like a drowned man, all desires but one driven from his head.

What ghostly kite floated on the still air like a great bird, the mighty wings as still as thought? Whose eye turned inward upon itself, searching for a lost view?

The king of Heaven, the fatherless child, wandered over the still sea, the place where air and water meet, seeking his dream in the tenuous film, the rainbow skin. In curling vagaries of mindless light he glimpsed the fleeting fantasy, running heels in a flower-rich meadow, flying hair, laughter unheard. Strange musk. He put his lips to a wave, and the wave was a breast. He dipped his arms in the sea, and his hands locked around a slim waist. Then the wave fell away and the vision was gone. Imperfect memory lost its grip on the flesh.

The nymph waited on the threshold of truth.

And Beltempest's eyes were closed. He rolled on the sea, turning in a half-sleep, wrestling with the vision. Silver hair, warm as a quilt, soft as down. Hot breath on his face. Wide eyes that came too close to look at. And blue, so very, very blue.

And the nymph-dream was shared among the brothers.

Glass lay face-down upon the soft clay, caressing the primal ooze. The vision swam before his closed eyes, and the sea-bed writhed beneath his body like a living thing, extruding limb-like round his neck. The delicious illusion of a mouth brushed his lips, and though his eyes were closed, he saw two wide eyes gazing into his own. Yellow. Too yellow for comfort.

9 TRIO

THREE BRIDES

The red moon, the yellow moon and the blue moon. First colours.

And the fatherless child looked down at the sea, flat as blue steel, polished like a mirror. So his own face gazed back, shifting, wandering, its contours losing certainty as he watched.

And closer, closer, till the four horns touched, when lightning scribbled in the air like a silver pencil. The dream spilled from his head.

The dream-nymph was a dream no more.

Two brown arms, slender and graceful as young fern-fronds, reached up from the waves, grasped him tenderly round the neck. And the dream-nymph drew herself out of the blue mirror, squeezed through a window between non-being and life. He took her in his arms, climbed into the air, held aloft the new-made miracle like a prize, a neat, brown body clothed only in spray and sunlight.

On her head were tiny horns.

This was the first female thing in all the Earth, and she sat upon his shoulder and sang. Red eyes she had like garnets, as red as her own red moon that rose even now like a beacon in the western sky, too red to look at for long.

And red shall have no spokesman.

For red can speak for itself.

The sixth moon set, and the fourth moon was turning the sky to yellow. Glass lay upon his sea-bed, fondling the shifting clay. Then two golden arms reached up from below, grasped him tenderly round the neck. And the dream-nymph drew herself out of the clay, squeezed through a hole between dreaming and waking. He took her in his arms, a golden treasure-chest, a pot of sweet honey. He took her to his house and set her on the roof. The three trumpets blared. The palace had a queen.

Yellow eyes she had. Too yellow to be true.

But colours need no clergy.

And shall any man tell you what is worshipful in yellow?

...squeezed through a window between non-being and life.

The fourth moon sank below the rim of the Earth, and the second moon was turning the sky to blue. No larks to sing, no distant bells. Not a cloud to stand between Beltempest and Heaven itself. Pale were the hands that reached down to him then from the air, a pale mother taking her child in her arms, drawing him through a gap in the hedge between death and life. The shepherd arose, no dream this. He blew on his horn and his bell chimed. The sky rejoiced and the flocks returned from the sea. Blue eyes she had, that spoke to the very heart.

And blue needs no interpreter.

Need any man tell you the meaning of blue?

So Beltempest knew his bride, and likewise did Glass in his kingdom below the sea. There was a blue moon and a moon of honey.

But the nymph with the red eyes waited, waited for the moon as red as an apple, and when it rose again she had her answer.

You shall be the bride of man, he said, *and queen of all the Dry Land. But first you must wait till man is made; first you must wait till the Dry Land itself rises from the deep.*

Then he hid her in a secret place, in a cave below the sea. Tenderly he touched the lids of her eyes, and made her sleep. The doll slumbered in her cradle. The pupa waited to be a moth.

The clock ticked. The great wheel turned.

The dream was spilling from his head like a tree, its mighty trunk cloven into a dozen branches, its great limbs splitting into narrow twigs. Eager, unthinking. Braided filaments, knotted strands. Off they scurried this way and that to the unknowable future, ravelled already beyond recall.

10 CHORALE

THE PEOPLING OF THE AIR

Beltempest's children. The birds, insects and spirits.

The sky was a pasture of sapphire. Beltempest lay with his bride in the blue grass, and his grazing flocks were all around. The clouds paid no heed, intent on their own affairs, bleating a monotone message to the sea. His strength was melted away, yet his pride was like new steel, for in this he was like a mortal man, weakened by longing, yet strengthened by love.

And they made a game of love and a game of war, in storms that trampled round the globe like a mighty army, with spears of lightning, drums of thunder; in wind, snow, rain and hail, and beneath them always the surging, heaving sea. Yet the warfare was only play, a masquerade, children squealing in the yard, a noisy sham. Sometimes thin as air, light as dryads in the wood, sometimes coarse and rough, furred like the goat. They could change at will, do you see? Their bodies would shift and melt, substance obedient to caprice.

Obedience spread like a forest fire. The very air took form, became flesh, became bird, or bat, or dragonfly, and every whim was clothed in light. New-made fairies clapped their hands, and the heavens shook. And their feet never touched the ground, untiring, needing only light and air for their strength, only the song of their father for a guide. No branches yet for the birds of the air; they roosted on the wing. No hive nor nectar yet for the honey-bees; the sky was house and larder for them all.

Night followed day. Day followed night. The seven moons rose and fell, rose and fell, bathing the Earth in a slow repetition of spectral colour. The rain would fall and the sweet wind blow. And the rainbow arched across the sky like a promise, like a lovely bridge from the sea to the sea.

And the children of the air were already ages old.

The very air took form, became flesh, became bird, or bat or dragonfly, and every whim was clothed in light.

11 SEA-SONG

THE PEOPLING OF THE WATER

The whales. The middle sea. The upper sea. The lower deep.

The ocean bed was honey-coloured clay, soft as silk. Hand in hand they lay, looking up at the place where air and water meet, watching the dim moons, the ripples, the shimmer, the slow, repeated passage of day and night.

Together they dreamed their own dreams, hand in hand, of mountains that could think, of gentle giants, of wise things, of fishes as big as clouds. And the dream was all the clay's command. It rose like a huge wave, rippled sunshine playing like a golden net upon its flanks. It shook. It heaved itself free. It burst from the clay, honey-coloured, a living creature. Huge fins appeared, and a tail. Then a smiling jaw and a small, wise eye on either side.

I look in at the eye of the giant, said Glass, *for his eye is the window of a room. And inside I see an old, old man, seated in an ancient study, full of wisdom, yet no older than today. How can this be?*

We walk on his shoulders, said the wife of Glass, *hand in hand like strollers on a hog-backed bill. One thousand paces is his measure from end to end, yet the water carries him like a cloud of thistledown. How can this be?*

Then the tail shook, and the fins beat down like huge wings. A living mountain flew through the sea like a bird, and the strollers tumbled from the hog-backed hill.

Shall we follow? cried Glass, becoming a fish.

To the ends of the Earth, laughed the wife of Glass, becoming the fish's wife.

But only upward, upward to the top of the sea did the great beast rise, flew to be nearer the rippling reflection of his own bulk, flew to the sacred place where air and water meet. Flew into illusion. Plunged into air. Then the surf erupted, white as frost, exploding light.

The short, thick moment drew itself out, impossibly thin.

The beast hung motionless in the air. Droplets of water made slow patterns all around him, poised,

And the children of the air were already ages old.

"I look in at the eye of the giant," said Glass, "for his eye is the window of a room."

turning playfully end over end. The rain waited to fall. Impossible. A marbled crater was yawning below, waiting for the monster to return. Impossible.

The small, wise eyes gazed sobrely out. The old, old man peered from his study window, hoped to see a pretty girl beckon from the edge of the wood. Saw no one. Returned to his books. And the beast slid back to the sea, slowly, like a monstrous tree. Then he snapped his mighty jaws and was gone.

And yet he has a wife, said the wife of Glass. *See, how his image peels from the mirror!*

For as he fell, the beast's reflection came to life, drawn through the door between being and non-being. Substance obedient to desire.

And they and all their kind peopled the middle sea forever, the new-born suckling at the breast like human young, wandering the ocean in families and races. The old, old men sang from their study windows, young as today, happy as dawn birds.

Glass and his wife wandered on the backs of the whales, passing from hill to hill, exploring a strange and shifting countryside, above them a green sea-sky, below them a green sea-deep.

Where are the fish of the upper sea? asked the wife of Glass. *And shall the lower deep be dumb?*

So the upper sea was filled with fishes, flocks of scaly birds too swift to catch. Gold and silver coinage spilled from the coffer of her mind. Substance obedient to the will.

To the dark sea-deep came water-worms and mole-fish, with eyes like wide topaz and flames upon their heads. Night in the city, yet lit by a billion lamps.

Not one of you shall flee, said Glass, *nor hide from your bigger brothers. There is nothing for you to fear in all our kingdom. Side by side you shall swim, and all your pursuit is play.*

So, to feed the creatures of the sea, there grew all kinds of greenery in great abundance, wandering clouds of drifting fern, floating prairies of sunlit grass, great trees rising from the very ocean floor. There were forests, so thick that even the whales must change their course and swim around. Secret, emerald groves where only sea-moss grew. Dark, lovely bowers where the mermaids sang.

So neither in the sky nor in the sea did any creature prey upon another, for all the Earth was innocent of death, and all her warfare only children's games.

Glass walked in the forests with his wife. Every fish was their child, every plant, every leaf. And they loved them. Yet when they tried to fix them with a name, to mark the branching rivers on a map, such tethers only broke, for every family changed to suit its changing home. The child shrugs off the parent's choice of clothes. Substance obedient to the need.

But what of the fatherless child? Did he sit on the edge of the void and watch? Did he neither covet his brothers' wives nor long for families of his own?

His dream grew dim, confused, fluttered like a butterfly on the edge of memory. He watched them walking in the great sea-wood, and those others playing with the clouds. He loved them. But he ached with love. Love was a sad, sad ache.

The dream would not come. He tipped the cask, he turned the tap. No ale. No ale.

So the sky and the sea made magic on their own. Nothing was planned. No grand design. Self-willed events attracted by the vacuum of an empty stage. And

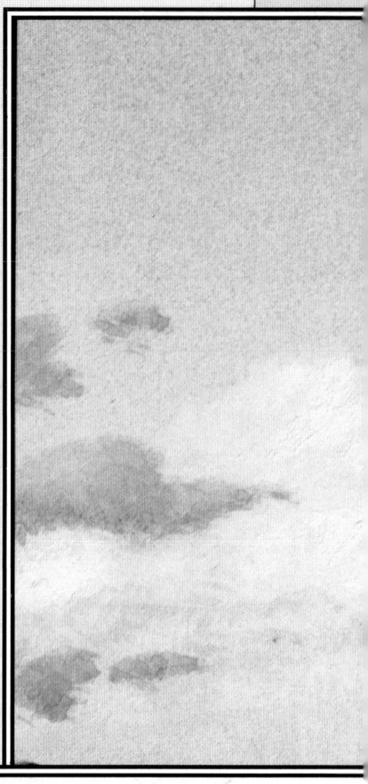

...the warfare was only play, a masquerade, children squealing in the yard, a noisy sham.

the empty stage was the sacred place where air and water meet, where the flocks of Beltempest walk from the water like pale ghosts, where the pretty raindrops dance and are gone.

A scaly hand emerged from the sea, explored the air, touched a downy breast and sank. A feathered arm dipped in the wave, caressed a finny shoulder and withdrew.

Our children woo the sea, said the wind, and held his breath.

Our children court the sky, whispered Glass, and held his tongue.

12 BARCAROLE

THE FLOATING CITIES

The meeting-place of air and water. A new race. Their cities.

And a new race arose, borne on that tenuous skin where the elements meet, at home in neither house, yet building a hovel in the alley in between. But their peoples flourished like lilies on a lake, and theirs were the first great cities on all the Earth.

Like men and women they were, two-legged and proud, and they rode on the sea in silver boats. They lived in floating green mansions, palaces that built themselves, not stone upon stone, but from the root like trees. There were nursery-towers and beacon-towers. Minstrels' gallery. Scholar's cell. And wiser even than the whales were those that gazed out to the broad horizon and saw their beacons mark their highways round the Earth.

Then all was safe and soundly made, and Beltempest breathed again. The salt breeze fluttered their fine clothes. Pennants flew on every tower. The wind blew and the waves grew. Yet the floating cities rode even the storm, for this is how the cities were made: the causeways did not break that linked one palace with another, for supple chains allowed each step to ride the swell. Each city had its wall, like a mighty ring of trees, a breakwater that banished the heaviest weather, and vast tracts of once-wild sea were enclosed like farmers' fields. Tame. Obedient. Fruitful. And rafts were built of sea-wood, pontoons and tenders, ships of strange design. The coloured buoys, like threaded beads, made frontiers on the undivided sea.

On windy nights the beacons seemed to march, rocking gently to and fro like a thousand swaying candlesticks, but when the nights were calm, they stood as motionless as the stars in Heaven. Each had its own signal, its own colour-sign, and even when the seventh moon hung alone like a black bomb in the night sky, there was many a friendly light to guide the wandering traveller home.

So the beacons made frontiers on the undivided sea, and every city was girdled by the living walls that kept the storm at bay. Through the gates of the cities came huge wooden ships back and forth, tall, proud, full of strange, exotic goods, fruits, spices, casks of foreign wines; and on the decks stood their scholars and

There were nursery-towers and beacon-towers. Minstrel's gallery. Scholar's cell.

their wise men, their kings and their queens, come to barter wisdom for wisdom, love for love.

We build a wall around the city, said the kings, *but none around the mind.*

We mark the frontiers with a beacon, said the queens, *yet have no frontiers in our hearts.*

And still no creature preyed upon another, nor yet pursued another for its food. All was found for them in the air and in the sea. Abundant. The trencher never empty, nor yet brimming over.

Inside the city walls there were broad, heaving fields, room enough for crops, room enough indeed for humble weeds and pretty vermin. The husbandman marched singing to his daily tasks. He ploughed, he sowed, he reaped, he pruned. His year was a busy round.

If you stitch me a seam or caulk my punt, said the husbandman, *you shall not go short of a loaf of bread.*

If you can sing or play, said the merchant, *then swap me a song for this bed and board.*

Now the people of the sea drank only salt water, and brine was in their blood. Not until man was made did any creature live by rain-water alone. So the people of the sea never called themselves men, though they were great in all the skills of men save one. And they drank salt water till the End of the World, when water, both salt and sweet, was gone for good.

And again, what of the fatherless child? Did he love all the people of the sea? Did he call their families his? His dream was teasing, hiding from him in the dark wood, tripping behind his back from tree to tree. Yes, he loved the people of the sea. But he loved the dream more. He ached with love. Love was a sad, sad ache.

The nymph with red eyes slept in a cave. Waited for man. Waited for the Dry Land that would rise up from the sea.

My dream is defaced by a nameless doubt, he whispered. *What mouse is this that nibbles in the dark, spoiling the unseen roundness of my cheese?*

And the dream came. He tipped the cask, he turned the tap. The dream poured forth. Not ale, but wine.

Prepare me a place, he said at last to the kings of the sea. *In each of your cities, before the gates, prepare me an open space, and let all your farmers come up from your fields and all your sailors out of your ships, and stand upon the ramparts with the wise men. For I will show you a special thing.*

13 AUBADE

THE MOTHERS OF MEN

Shells from the sky. They hatch. The nests in the cities.

So all the people did as he told them, and at the door of every kingdom lay a field of empty sea. The watchers gathered on the city walls, hushed, excited, overcome.

The sky flew open like a door, and all at once the child of the void stood on the threshold, a ragged orphan begging from house to house.

My cradle is my tomb, he cried. And all the people trembled. *I am the only eye in an endless night. Though I build the stars with a flick of my tail, though I hold the Earth in my hand, though I break the very universe with my horn, I cannot make me a mother or a father to tread my path before me. Not even for me shall the wheel run backwards, nor the sand of time spring upward from the lower glass.*

And all the people stood on the city walls and wept.

In your lives shall I seek my own, he said, *and in your families shall I have my kin-folk.*

Then our lives are yours, said the people of the sea, *and all our children too.* And they wept again, till silenced by a mighty roar, for the door from Heaven was closing with a bang, and the orphan from the sky had come into his own.

His huge wings covered them. His tail reached round the whole Earth. The child had become a giant, strong in the arm, joyful in his sleight of hand. He juggled with the air, too quick to see. Magic. And where did they come from, those falling shells that he scattered upon the water? Who saw the magic sleeve, the magic hat? For in the empty sea at the gate of each city there appeared a purple boat, shell-like, with curling prow and stern.

Here is my gift to every city, he said. *These are my chickens. Count them as they hatch.*

And the orphan stepped back into the night and was gone. The sky-door closed.

The shells stood motionless in the still water, their upper parts shrinking slowly in the sun. Then silently, as all the people watched from the city walls, the drying skin began to split. Ripening fruit. Unfurling wrappings. Parting lips.

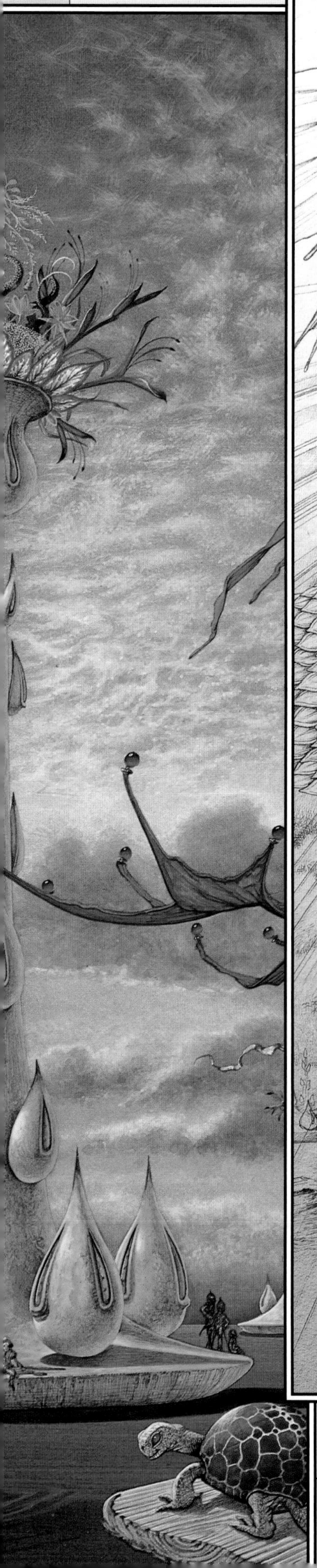

"Here is my gift to every city,"
he said. "These are my chickens."

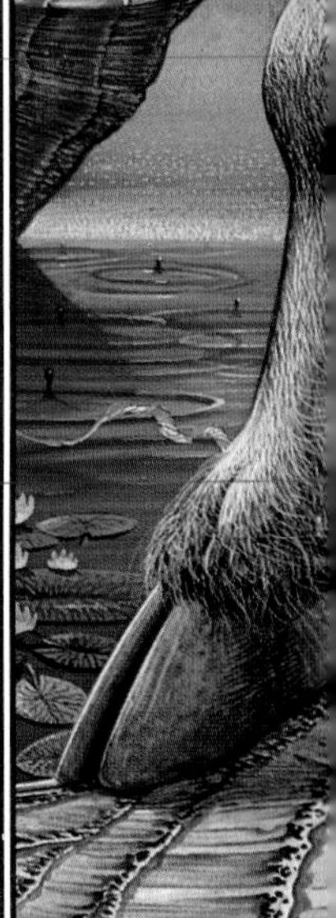

...she blew a long, shrill fanfare for the risen Sun.

Then, horned like a god, hoofed and hairy as a goat, something drew itself uncertainly from the egg, a lovely flying thing, feathered like a bird, sweet and soft as a young girl. The wings were like green silk, and from each flight-feather stared a single eye, gentle and trusting as a deer's. A flute of gold was in her hand, and with it she called to her sisters across the sea. From every far-flung city came a shrill reply.

I am the mother of man, said the flute to the city gates. *I stand before you and wait.*

So the people of the sea opened up the gates of their cities, but the green wings flew above their ramparts, needing no open door.

I am the mother of man, said the flute to the rolling fields. *Where shall I build my nest?*

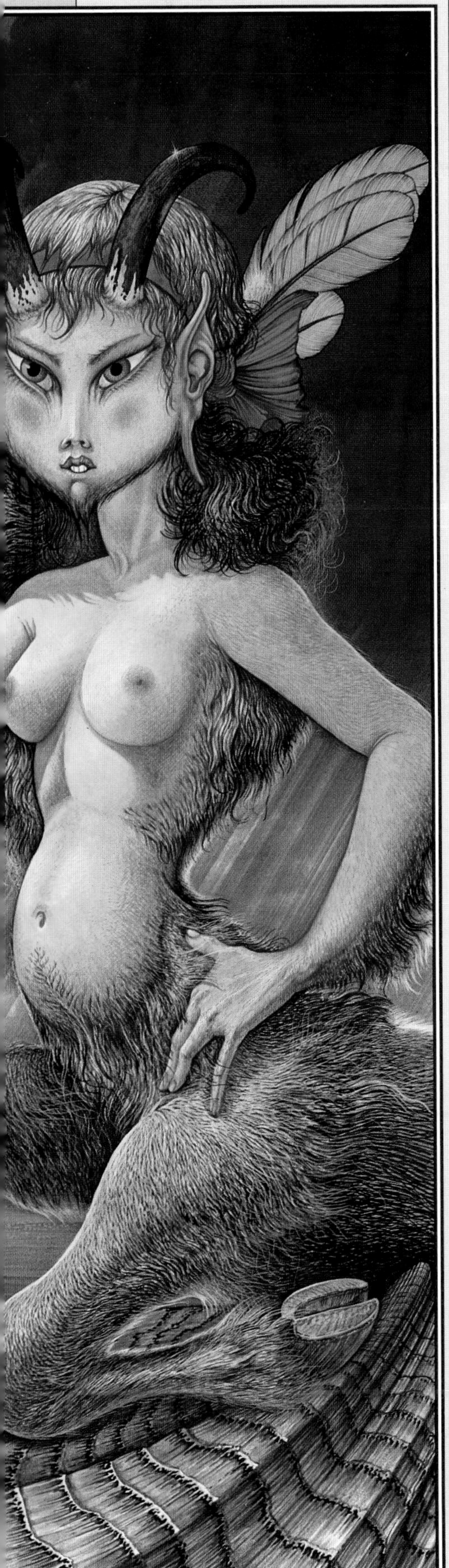

And the purple shells filled with a sudden rain, sank to the bottom of the sea, became homes for the vagrant fish, the hermit-crab.

So the mother of man lived in the field like a farmyard pet, and the same was in every city. And from all their towers the people came down to watch her build her nest. Of reeds and grass and braided sticks she made it, lined it with moss and soft leaves. Then, covered by her velvet wings, she slept. And the eyes on her lovely feathers watched as the orange moon plunged after the Sun and followed her mistress into the sea.

Then the sixth moon rose, blood red, flooding the whole Earth with her baleful glow. The eyes watched, unblinking, feathers defiantly green in the all-pervading crimson.

You shall not have him, said the mother of man to the red moon.

And when Darkness hung in the sky alone...

He is mine, said the night.

No bird sang. No fish jumped. The minstrel slept in the palace hall. Only the lonely watchman stood at the gate-house lamp, snuffer in hand, and waited for the Sun to rise again.

There came a slow pallor along the horizon. The lowest golden clouds peeped over the edge of the sky, already burning with a fire that would soon engulf them all. The watchman doused his light. The lamps were winking off along the highways of the world. A flute sounded from the East, shrill and clear. In the next city day had already come.

Below the tower its long green shadow reached across the field. The grass heaved with a gentle swell, the relic of a distant storm, a drama played out days ago and far away. The green feathers stirred around the high nest, the eyes shuffled, unblinking in the new day-glow. Then she raised herself on her hind-legs, spread her broad, translucent wings, and flew up from the nest. The morning sunshine painted her feathers with new, fresh colours. Then, touching the flute to her girlish mouth, she blew a long, shrill fanfare for the risen Sun. And from the West, where dawn was still a promise, came the answering call of her nearest sister.

From his high, high garret the lonely watchman spied into the nest. Saw nothing. Left his post. And the same was in every city.

14 INTROIT

MAN

The first men. The people of the sea care for them. The mothers go.

And so the weeks passed by. And every day the people of the sea would come across the fields to view the nest or to bring small gifts. Like a queen she sat, her feathers like a royal gown. The people stared, not understanding, overcome by a strange love. The eyes upon her wings stared blindly back.

And every day from his high tower the watchman spied into her nest. Saw nothing. Left his post. And the same was in every city.

But then the fifth moon rose again, and the night was the colour of dull brass. The beacons were scarcely needed, flickered thinly like candles in the day. Then the Sun herself came up. The white ox came to turn the wine-press.

From his high, high garret the lonely watchman spied into the nest.

At this point in the narrative — of many versions at least — there is a complete gap. In the principle source several tablets have gone completely missing. In others there are deletions and/or corrections. All the accounts which remain intact differ considerably on this one issue — the precise physical origin of man. For the purposes of this book however, we have assembled a composite, omitting such details as occur in only one version.

It seems that when the Sun eventually rose on the fortieth day, each nest contained three eggs. This number is not in dispute, having obvious significance in relation to other triads in the story, though many texts disagree about the colour of the eggs. In some they are black, in others white, and in one fanciful version each egg is even given a primary colour — red, blue, yellow — obviously a reference again to the three kingdoms, of Beltempest, Glass and man.

After several days the eggs hatch, the Kashrinn (— this is the phonetic, non-ideographic name for the "mothers of men") blow a flute fanfare, and each nest is found to contain three babies. Oddly enough no mention is made of the colour of the babies. Some accounts describe the confusion of the sea-birds on hearing the babies' raucous cries, most agree that they were suckled at the breast of the Kashrinn, few omit long, sentimental paragraphs about the tenderness and sweet emotions aroused among the sea-people, and all (perhaps not surprisingly — after all the books were written by humans) give long accounts of the amazing and precocious talents of the newcomers.

No doubt at some point in their history, our ancestors must have suffered heated controversies over their origins. Perhaps it was considered somewhat inappropriate for man to have emerged from an egg, or perhaps the idea was dismissed as preposterous by some ancient forerunner of Darwinism. At all events, only one version of the story describes man as a blood relative of the creator.

The story continues...

"Three Shells" — fruit-juice analogue.

Each time the brass moon rose, pursued by the moon of copper, a new man-brood was born, and the people of the sea took the yearlings into their own homes, caring for them among their own children. They gave them bread, whale-milk, fruit from the trees, and because of their special need, fresh rain-water funnelled from the roof. The tiny hand played in the tiny mouth, soft and meek, a comfort to the soul.

When the eldest man-children saw their tenth year, the last brood came to their first, and their handsome mothers, barren now, gave their milk for the last time.

From the void the motherless child looked on, his joy second-hand, the warmth in his heart tainted by an unbidden sadness. The tender breast was sweet work, such helpless infancy sublimest poesy.

Would that I were a mere man, cried the maker of the universe, *that such a tenderness might enfold me and keep me from the night. It wants but the span of his mother's hand, and a man may hide the black moon from his eyes. But though I close my eyes I see it still. Through the mountain. Through the very Earth itself.*

Whereupon the work was done. They forsook their nests, leaving the children in the houses of the sea-people. There gathered a great flock, circling in the high air like migrant birds, and the clamour of their wings was heard far below in the floating cities.

What shall become of them? cried the people. *Where is their home? What shall be their food?*

But they lived in the clouds even to the latter days, sleeping on the wing, and their hooves trod the unseen pastures of the sky. For Beltempest keeps them. They are his. They hide among his flocks like strange, green sheep. Their flutes may be heard in the clouds. Birdsong in thunder.

15 TOCCATA

THE DRY LAND

The city of men. They are brought to the Dry Land.

They sat in their stone pews and waited for the word of God.

So much for man. All was found for him among the people of the cities. The children were loved and cherished, were taught all the skills and arts that the sea-folk knew. Quick to learn, the apprentice soon outstripped his master.

A city of ships. A city of men. They gathered from every place, assembled for some promised purpose. They were tall and proud, a noble race, each man the captain of his soul, the admiral of his venturing dreams. They bound their ships one to another like logs upon the river, and soon a great new city, broader than all others, spread across the ocean like a continent. It was a city of wood and rope, a maze of decks and planking, a forest of masts and sails. The decks were like streets, full of bustling commerce, and below the decks were all their stores for years of exile on the sea.

Only men lived within the ships, for even now mankind was male in every part, and every man was alone in his head with impossible dreams. The harbourside cottage, bright-eyed children chuckling over the wicket-gate to meet him, the wife smiling in the doorway... beautiful... between the cottage and the green hills, bright creepers in the hedge, a row of beans... the fertile soil. The Dry Land waited in the dream.

By air and by sea the scouts were sent abroad. And some returned in weeks and some were gone for years. No news. No news. For even now the Earth was ocean from end to end, and there was neither sand nor stone anywhere upon it.

And the Dry Land was made. Of clay from the ocean floor and of the fire within it. The kiln baked its own brick walls. Slowly it rose from the deep, heaving, layer upon layer, piling itself into the sky, a great stone beast forever heaping rocks upon its own back. The gentle clouds were shouldered aside. Quick lightning flickered in the steam that rose from its wet heat, for the stone beast was hot with sweat. Its substance flowed like golden fire, congealed like crimson blood. It stiffened, froze, then cracked apart again, spewing forth hot streams of lava that flowed once more to the boiling sea.

The making of the Dry Land was wild dispute, unpredictable, the quarrel of a thousand incompatibilities of chemistry. Yet its very torment built it, made it strong. The beast had a fever. It shivered. It shook. Yet somehow the fever made it grow.

The mountains filled the sky like rows of stalléd giants. Thunder was all their deafening argument, and the muffling snow damped their whispered conversations. They sat in their stone pews and waited for the word of God.

And the Dry Land was made…

Its substance flowed like golden fire…

But who should come but a child to play? No minister to his chanting congregation.

And he rejoiced in the Dry Land, the battling of the fire and water, the dispute of ice and snow, the squabble of earth and air. The Dry Land was more restless than the sea, more dynamic even than Heaven. So he amused himself on the Dry Land, as a child might play on a beach. He built castles in the sand. He smashed his castles down. He built temples of stone and palaces of ice. With careful fingers he moulded their traceried vaults. Then, with one blow of his mighty horn, he laid them waste. Exultant. And built again.

"Here is your home and your heritage," he said, and he led them to the shore and left them.

But what of man? said the watchman to the sky. *Shall his destiny be forgot?*

And what of me? said the bride of man. *What of my destiny? Shall I sleep forever in my dark cell? Shall I die before I live?*

The reproach darkened the world. The story was only half told, and the story-teller seemed weary of his own words. He nodded in his chair, confused, the threads of his saga tangling in his head. For want of a certainty he paused...

The reproach darkened the world. The dream was only half made-real, and the dreamer seemed about to sleep again. He dozed on a mountain's brink, the dream-vision closing up his eyes. For want of a certainty he paused...

And all at once something wakened him, quickened both his memory and his answering limbs. The child of the void came down at last from the mountain, and he went to the place where all the ships were bound together on the sea. His limbs were heavy, his eyes yearned for sleep, yet nevertheless he led the men to the Dry Land.

Here is your home and your heritage, he said, and he led them to the shore and left them. No word more. No understanding. The dark wings filled the sky, could hardly move. The mighty tail flicked like a tired snake. Suddenly he was gone.

The world was on its own.

16 DIRGE

FIRST DEATH

The ships are destroyed. The tides.
The Dry Land is unsafe.

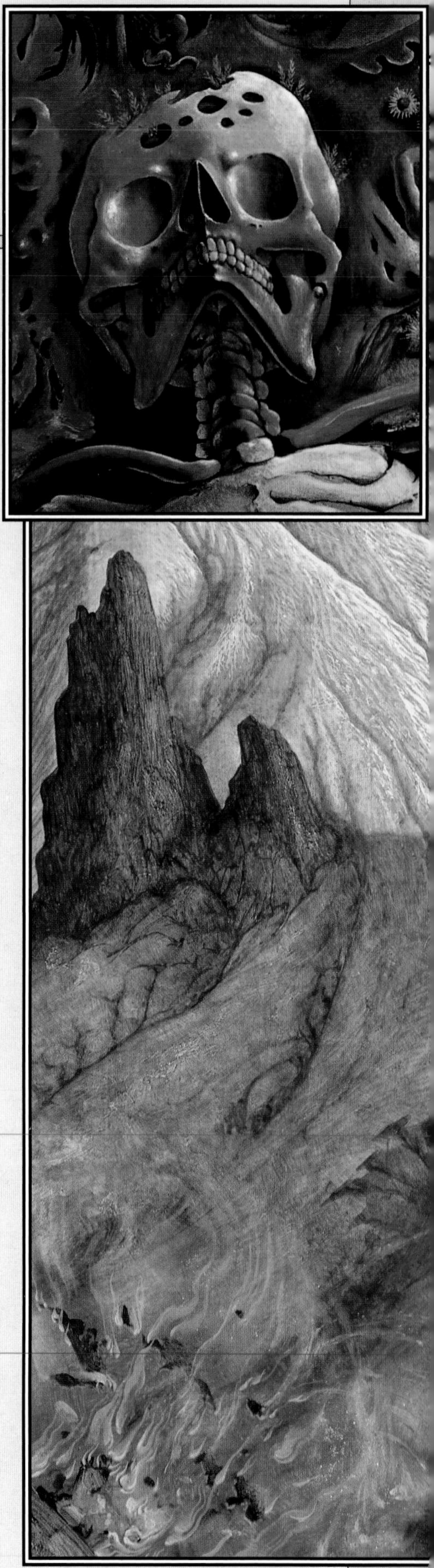

For Death was new, unbelieved-in, too young to have a name.

The men came down from their ships and set foot on the new ground. Here and there it was hot enough to set fire to the soles of their shoes, while elsewhere the ice flowed slowly from the mountains in thick and faulted streams, impossible to cross. And yet the men were glad to come down from their ships. They set off in search of habitable places amid all the fire and fog. Had they not built a city on the sea? Might they not just as easily build one on the land?

But the Dry Land was not a safe place for men. Where the giants play giants' games, let the weak beware.

The moons, like seven oxen, hauled the seething waters across the flat lands, sometimes higher, sometimes lower. For the tides were unknown before there was land, an unseen rising and falling, harmless to all. But the land quarrelled with the tides, stubborn, unpredictable, deadly. And the ships went down by the hundred, broken upon the rocks, scattered across the beaches. And so was lost the store-house of all their wealth, their books, their instruments, their tools. Gone was all record of their past, all written knowledge, and with it all hope of the future. The tides had destroyed all their seed and grain.

And so came unnamed Death into the world, and men were the first things on all the Earth to die. Not by malice. Not by neglect. They were destroyed only by the blind, unthinking Earth. For the Earth is blameless clockwork, too great, too orderly, to intricate to care.

And those that came safely to the shore found only the mockery of refuge, for the Dry Land was not a finished work. Fire and smoke burst from the ground, slaughtering the frightened men with poisonous mists and thunderstorms of hot ash.

Weeping with fear and grief, they cried to the sky for help. Yet no hand came down to them from the void, for the sleep was almost upon him at that time and he did not hear.

Honey and fruit had been their customary food. From the cradle to manhood, milk and fresh water their special portion. What must they eat now but bitter

moss, tough grass and perfidious fungi? And many died by eating dangerous food. Thin corpses marched to unmarked graves, blind, unlovable in death.

For Death was new, unbelieved-in, too young to have a name.

The young man shook his brother's shoulder, propped his lifeless corpse against a rock. What sleep was this that would not yield to cries, nor to blows from a stick, nor yet to hot, loud tears?

The cold of the night killed hundreds more. The Cold was a blind executioner; no mere blanket held him off, no meagre shelter stayed the falling of his unseen axe. The Cold killed without passion, without cruelty, without mercy.

Others warmed themselves at night where the rock spewed molten from the ground, then, overwhelmed by inattentive sleep, they tumbled one by one, cremated in the twinkling of an eye. And the mindless lava heaved and bubbled with pseudo-life, taking them unto its own dead substance, melting the well-loved face, the well-loved hand, the precious, mysterious mind.

Some brave men there were that clung to blind hope and their own resource. They made crude hovels for the night, with small slabs of stone for the walls and greater slabs for the roofs. And they hid in their hovels and cowered.

The Dry Land was like a sleeping stallion that dreamed it gallopped in the meadow. Its skin twitched and shuddered; buried muscles half-responded to the dream. When the bed-rock shook, the marl above it trembled, shaking the stone houses to ruins; and the people died by the thousands, buried under cairns they had built with their own hands.

So those few that remained went naked and cold, crouching in whatever caves and fissures they could find in the unforgiving stone. As they died, they remembered how they had lived, their frightened souls walking backwards through the years, trying to escape the horror of the present in memories of the past. They dreamed of soft, warm down, the feel of green feathers, joyful sky-rides on their mothers' soaring backs.

How far away, how impossible is the past. Never more than a memory.

17 LAMENT

THE AGE OF ICE

Beltempest visits the Dry Land. He looks for man. His anger.

But all around them walked mindless Death. Her breath was the smell of burning flesh, her dried-up bosom was the cold, unfeeling ground. Thousands froze in their stony cells, their shrivelled corpses stiff and white with rime.

And on the edge of the world the fatherless child dreamed on, like a sand-boy asleep at the top of the beach, unaware of the turning tide. His once-proud sand-castles were flattened. His lead soldiers were losing their war.

The creatures of the air were afraid of the Dry Land, its mountains, fire and ice. All their merry multitude were long gone. Neither at the shore was any sea-creature to be seen — no fish, no whale — for all the ocean's bestiary were in danger from the tides. So the men suffered and died, unseen except by their brothers in sorrow. And their mothers played in the clouds on the other side of the Earth.

The sand-boy slept.

The doll waited in her cave.

And the lead soldiers were losing their war with the tide, drowning one by one.

Only the bell-wether, only Beltempest himself dared visit the new kingdom. His tired flocks bleated after him over the mountains. Thunder drummed and lightning rattled, for the summits squabbled with the air, must guard their frontiers by war. So Beltempest stood upon the peaks, looked down in wonder on all the new world that was made. Cities of stone, highways of ice, fountains of flame, pillars of smoke.

Great indeed is man, he said, *that such wonders can be at his command.* For he knew that the Dry Land was man's kingdom, just as he was ruler of the air and Glass was governor of the sea. The hills, he thought, were hollow. The men must live within, mighty men indeed to live in such great houses. So he went about all over the land, looking for a place where he could see the men at work or watch their children playing in the rooms of stone.

And the mindless lava heaved and bubbled with pseudo-life.

He was a golden giant, the good shepherd of the clouds.

He marched above the rock and sand. He took for sport the treacherous tides, the crumbling cliffs, the long and shifting estuaries of mud. From cape to cape he went, treading the tumbled rocks, the tormented surf. He strode the high, mist-shrouded slopes where all the rain was sucked from the northern wind. He crossed the great broad plains where wave upon wave of blown sand marched ever southwards like a heat-frozen sea.

And every noise was only lonely noise. The whisper of sand whispering to sand, the quarrel of mindless rock, the roar of pseudo-living fire. He found no palace-gate, no window in the mountain. Of man there was no trace, neither house nor ship, nor yet a blurry foot-print on the sand.

I leave my tracks along the shore, he said, *and the tide shall wash away all trace — even of me. What mark might a man make in such a wilderness as this?*

Whereupon he came to the very place where the dead men lay. And when he saw them scattered on the ground, their frail bodies broken, their eyes all blank and still in death, Beltempest was afraid.

A cold, cold hand was clawing at the sky, a dream-hand, a hand from some other time and place. And he knew that one day even he would come to this.

The world was learning death. The world was already ages old.

The dead men would not wake. Beltempest tolled his bell. He blew on his horn, and all the high peaks shook. He sang like a lonely child. Tears ran down the mountainside. The Dry Land sobbed. And still the men would not wake.

What manner of king is this, he cried, *that is brought to nothing in his own kingdom? What is this country of man that all his wealth is swallowed up and comes to naught?* And he took the dead men tenderly in his arms and wept.

Whereupon the few men that were left alive came weakly from their caves and from their fissures in the rock, and above them in the dazzling sky the storm-god stood, his foot upon the distant hill, his foot upon the nearer shore. The night had come to where they were, and yet the bright Sun still gilded his mighty horns. He was a golden giant, the good shepherd of the clouds. Huge, a mighty magic.

But the good shepherd was learning death.

And even the storm-god was dumb, for death is a hard lesson.

Was this part of the dream? he cried, his anger flickering on his horns. *And shall a clockwork hangman stop the game, and sweetness turn to sourness at the end?*

His great knees split the sea. He strode the tide-riven shore. He gathered in his arm every last man that was left alive upon the Dry Land; like sheaves of pale corn he gathered them, weak, as white as frosted twigs. And he bore them to the people of the sea, to the floating cities, and left them in their care.

And so it was that man was saved, though naught could save the thousands that were dead.

Beltempest turned his tears to ice. His playful warfare turned to wrath. A thick, dull snow fell upon the Dry Land, buried the desert shores in deep, deep white. The rivers froze within their beds, the cataracts were stairways of ice. Even the hot ground became cold, the flowing magma thickening in the wound like blood. And still the snow deepened. A white nothing. And all the Dry Land was buried in white like an unloved memory.

Die! whispered the wind, *since you brought Death into the world.*

And never rise again! said the sea, and made a wall of ice to seal it up.

And still the dream was in the cask. The dreamer held the cup. He turned the tap. The dream poured forth. Not wine, but vinegar.

He awoke to find himself accused.

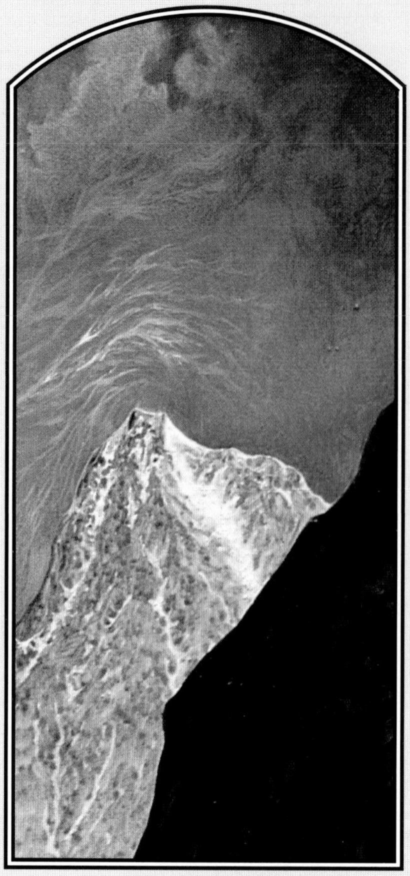

A thick, dull snow fell upon the Dry Land...

18 HALLELUJAH

THE DRY LAND RE-MADE

The dreamer awakes. His grief. The seasons. The land becomes good.

The wind told the sad tale; the wind itself accused him. Faint echoes of hopeless pain circled the Earth to whisper in his ear.

Where was your hand, said the wind, *when your children went astray? And where was your ear, when all men cried to you?*

Yet no answer came but silent grief, no plea but wordless shame. And the child of the void sat upon the Dry Land and wept, and with him was Beltempest his brother, accuser turned comforter. For all that lives must rest, and all that lives must die, and all the living things there are, from the smallest fish to the gods themselves, must one day come to naught. And mighty Beltempest comforted the child that had made him, and all the world waited, as grief was turned to sadness, and shame to iron resolve.

The Earth spins upon his finger-end. He tips it like a slowing top, distributes sunshine like a boon among the people.

And so there were seasons upon the Earth, and the Dry Land was changed. The ice and snow melted away. The hills were gentler, softened with a carpet of grass. In every part there was green, triumphant green. It soothed the eye, too green to be believed. There were thickets, lawns, spinneys, forests, and everywhere flowers of every colour.

My colours need no herald, said the forest king.
Need any man be told which colour is king?

A pleasant wonderland was the Dry Land by now, a beautiful garden that needed neither husbandman nor steward, for all its ways were a motive to themselves, and every cup was replenished of itself. The seasons turned in coloured splendour. Summer decked the trees with bright flowers, and Autumn's magic turned the flowers to coloured fruit.

So the birds of the air had a roosting-place at last, and the honey-bees came down into their own.

And still the dream was in the cask. The dreamer sipped, then drained his cup. No vinegar this, but only nectar in his mouth.

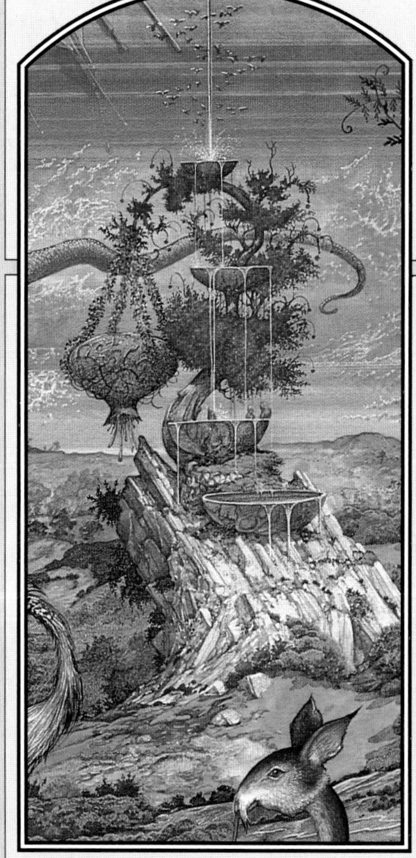

So the birds of the air had a roosting-place at last, and the honey-bees came down into their own.

And all its ways were a motive to themselves…

...and every cup was replenished of itself.

19 PASTORALE

THE BEASTS OF THE DRY LAND

The commonwealth of man and beast. Peace and happiness.

He paused to find the fittest thought, he chose his word with care. Lest trouble unforeseen should spoil the dream. And substance was obedient to the word.

So the beasts were made that lived on the Dry Land. There were hairy beasts and scaly beasts, and some were small and others large, and some lived in the forests and others in the grassland, each to his own place and to his given food. And the garner never emptied, nor yet brimmed over.

Not one of you shall flee, said man, *nor hide from me. There is nothing for you to fear in all my kingdom. Side by side we shall walk and all our pursuit is play.*

So not in the sky, nor in the sea, nor yet upon the Dry Land itself did any creature prey upon another, for all the Earth was innocent of Death, and all her warfare only children's games.

Yet Death still lived in the shame of the fatherless child, and in Beltempest's secret heart, and in the deep, deep memory of man. A cold hand, an eyeless face, an open jaw.

Leave me, leave me, said man to the dead ear, *that I may live my life in joy.*

And Death found a secret place to hide, a cave beneath the sea, where a forgotten nymph longed to be a bride. Together they slept, Death and the Maiden, twin pupae learning to be moths. Side by side. Cheek to cheek.

The beasts of the Dry Land became the friends of man.

His kingdom was a commonwealth, and the king was only one of many.

Is not the horse the monarch of the plains, said man, *and yet the lowly snail is governor in the grass? Is not the squirrel master in the tree,* he said, *and yet the humble worm is governor in the wood?*

And the beasts were his family and his friends and all his company. He shared their thoughts and knew their needs. He cared for them. They cared for him.

"There is nothing for you to fear in all my kingdom. Side by side we shall walk and all our pursuit is play."

"Keep her for your own, that all the children of the Dry Land shall know their own fathers and mothers and love them."

20 LOVE-SONG

WOMAN

The dream is made flesh. Man and woman together. Sleep returns.

So the child of the void was glad, for all the Dry Land was a happy place. And he loved the men, the birds, the beasts of the wood. And the dream hid from him in the dark wood, tripping behind his back from tree to tree. Yes, he loved the Dry Land. But he loved the dream more. He ached with love. Love was a sad, sad ache.

And here is how the fruit went bad. It was not by malice, nor by deliberate fault, nor yet by negligence. The world was spoiled through love. Paradox. Impossible. And yet it was so.

For the child of the void pursued his dream in the wood, and the dream fluttered in the corner of his eye. In the wood there was a quiet place, scented with fresh bracken, the brown earth underfoot upholstered with soft leaves. For a space of time he became a man, and walked two-legged in the musk-scented forest, though his spirit could hardly hold the form, and he came and went like a ghost.

Like a ghost he lay on the leafy forest floor, a ghost come to lie with a ghost. Her hair was spun gold. Her flesh was smooth, pungent, downy as a peach. She sat chastely at his side, her hand nestling in his like a warm chick, for although the dream of her was old, the fact of her was new, as new as a china doll still hot from the kiln, as golden and sweet-smelling as bread fresh from the oven.

Yet he did not make her. Not make her as a man might make a doll or a loaf of bread. His hand never moulded her thigh, nor turned her breast, nor yet sculpted her delicate ear. No, only by his thinking was she made. Substance obedient to the dream. And so she sat chastely at his side as he slept, a real creature, with a heart and lungs, with a mind and thoughts of her own, and every part of her shape knew its place and kept itself whole. That was the hidden art of all living things, that every piece of skin and every smallest hair should know its own shape and have a memory of its purpose. For no creature is described from outside. Only from a hidden book within itself shall a living thing read its own destiny.

...all the Dry Land was a happy place.

For no creature is described from outside. Only from a hidden book within...

And so it was with woman and all her kind. They came from a dream, and the dream within them kept them whole. Substance obedient to love.

And the child of the void went to sleep. Heavy and dark was his sleep, the sleep of an old, old man, a man whose dream is so bright that he awakes only to a shadow. And if you should look for the sleeper in the wood, you shall never find him. No ancient giant lies buried under the moss and mouldering leaves. There is no cairn to mark the sleep of ages. He is gone. Not dead, just gone away. Risen like a mist, blown to the four winds like smoke, as insubstantial as air.

Thus was woman made. And thus, like a midnight nursery, was all the world left to its own devices. As the child's eyes slowly closed, so did the toy-cupboard slowly open. The clockwork Pierrot came to dance with the clockwork Columbine.

Yet none of the toys had clockwork hearts, and their movements were driven by something shrewder than the simple winding of a spring.

So the women came to the men in the forests and loved them.

And the ghost turned in its sleep, whispering: *Let no man be short of a wife,* he said, *to be queen of his heart. Keep her for your own, that all the children of the Dry Land shall know their own fathers and mothers and love them. Your home is a safe home. By your husbandry may you keep it so for all time. My part is done.*

So the whole Earth was happy, loud with joy and song, and every element was ordered for the good of all, in the sky, in the sea and on the Dry Land.

But you may say: *What of Death? How did they live and breed, and feed upon the plenty of the Earth, and live and breed again, yet never die?*

And I shall say: Impossible. Yet it was so, for time itself was different then. Slow as the stars, the families of men spread across the Dry Land, and just as the racing galaxies found no frontier in space, so did the measure of the Earth never fail to meet the needs of her children. Impossible. Yet it was so. We have no words.

Time itself was different then.

21 DISSONANCE

THE FORGOTTEN BRIDE

The nymph awakes and breaks free.
Her jealousy and her anger.

...through this small, small door shall evil creep into the world and every malice into the mind.

And here is how the bad fruit rotted.

Where there is wrong without redress, where there is suffering without comfort, so — whether the fault be deliberate or not — through this small, small door shall evil creep into the world and every malice into the mind.

For in a cave at the bottom of the sea the doll still slept her long night, impatient for her dawn. She was not unloved, was not forgotten. And yet she changed, as all things do that think themselves unloved. Her hands were on her breast, palms together. Like a young girl at prayer she lay, living only in her own mind. And above her was the hard and mindless rock, and above the mindless rock the very sea itself.

Ten centuries were too long for sleep, too long even for dreams. Whatever palaces she had — her gardens, her pretty children — they were nothing more than pictures in the mind. As ten centuries passed for mankind, a thousand years of careless joy, for the same thousand years her feet touched only cold stone, her cheek only the cold cheek of Death.

For Death was with her in the cave, a cold machine, waiting. Unaware of waiting.

Like a sickly child she struggled in her sleep, swimming up through the waters of her mind, wrestling with the unseen horror that shared her bed. And when she awoke at last, she knew that she had been forgotten.

Yet found herself not alone.

Who can say how she broke free? Did she smash her stall like a wild bull? Did she leap from the pit like a deer? Did she burst her chains by the unknown strength of the innocent accused, by the power of mind on metal? Substance dissolved by anger?

Who can say how she came forth? Did the rock break with her flaming sword? Was the sea turned to steam? No man shall ever know it, only that she came.

Did she smell the rivers like a salmon? Did the fresh water sing to her of land? Did she swim? Did she fly? No man shall ever know it, only that she came.

And was not alone.

So she came to the Dry Land, for this was her promised kingdom. She came to man, for he was her promised husband.

And she found herself betrayed. There were palaces indeed in her kingdom, yet every palace had a mistress. There were gardens indeed, yet the blossom was not for her to gather. And pretty children played in the gardens, not one of them hers, not one of them bearing her mother-mark.

I see your happy states, she cried. *I see your kinships and your friendships. Your hearths are warm and your bellies are round with babies. What part is mine in all this show?*

Oh, you happy mothers, she cried. *I see your husbands, and I love them. I see your babies at your breast and my nipple weeps milky tears. Where is my place at your feast?*

What choice have I, in loving them, but to hate you?

22 PERCUSSION SOLO

MALICE

The massacre of the women. The curse of forgotten tongues.

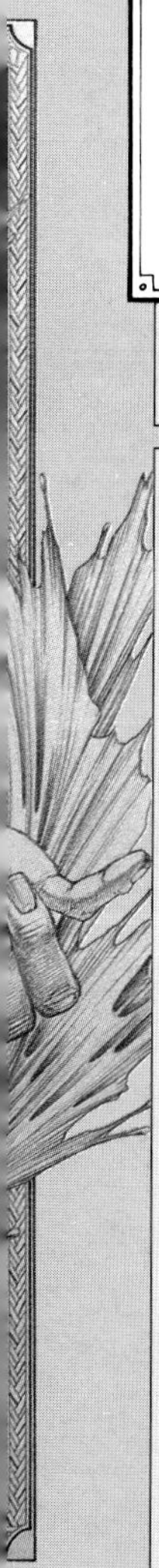

And she went away into the wood, her cheek scalded by her own tears. An angry hand might smash an oak, and yet she took only the branch of a yew-tree for her weapon. Hatred might lift a forest by its roots, and yet she took but the withies from the hazel to be her arrows. A bow and arrows she made in the wood, which was the first weapon of any kind upon the Earth.

A squirrel watched her as she worked, curious, trustful as all beasts were. She clubbed it with a stick. Braided skin and gut made a bow-string. The squirrel seemed to watch her still, though its eyes would never see again. Blood stained the dry leaves on the forest floor. The birds still sang.

So she became mistress of the dark places, there being no heritage for her in the light. And she reached her hand into the darkness, exploring unreality by touch. For darkness is a horn of plenty, full of all possibilities. It is the hand alone, when reaching in, decides what fictions should be turned into facts. And guided by her blackened heart, her hand chose only nightmare, horror and evil. She led them out from darkness like a sad procession, beasts without minds, a dull army of torture and subjection. The wasp that plunders the honey-comb, the tick that gnaws at the swallow's wing, the lesser worm that dwells within the greater worm — blind torturers every one. And all her creatures were her slaves, great and small, a *subtle state* at war with man.

In a world where fear had been unknown, she ruled by fear.

In a world innocent of death, killing became her delight. She ruled in her state by an alien law.

And the name of her law was Pain.

I see my mark upon your breasts, she cried to the women, *and you shall be the first to die by killing in all the world.*

And so the sweet women perished, stricken by the arrows from her bow, till only a small number of them remained, herded like innocent cattle, fattened for ritual death, saved for her special tortures, for feasts and for holy days.

Hatred might lift a forest by the roots...

"The beginning of strife, the beginning of death."

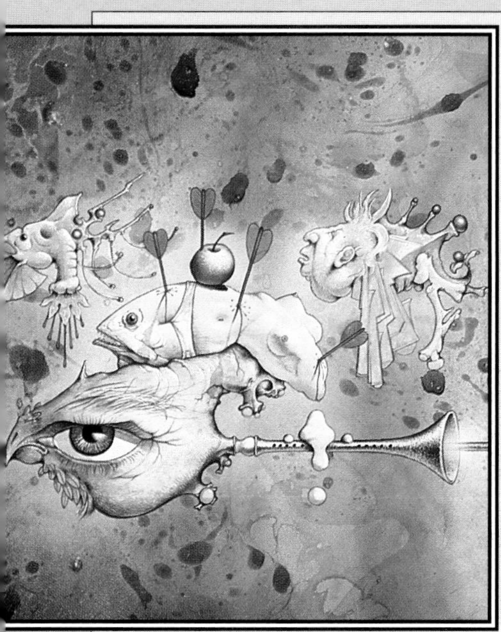

"...all the creatures shall forget their words, lost for the calls that make them one nation."

And so came the law of Pain to govern mankind, for by fear of Death she could rule him with a feather, and by Pain she could teach him any tricks.

She had no need of flattery, yet it pleased her to beguile him by playing upon his pride.

Your hand is wasted in the forest, she whispered. *What need is there for skill when all is found for you?*

So the men set to burning the forest and clearing it away, and in the clearings they built cities of stone and wood, towers, mansions, highways, a shrine to the tyrant and a pageant of their own vainglory. In every town she lived, a spirit queen in a house of painted glass, and in every town she plotted a long, slow game. The long, slow torture of man.

The cities grew like bright thickets, loud by day, busy by night, and bright with a billion lamps. And the men that built the cities lost sight of their old ways, forgot the lovely past like a fleeting dream.

It was never any other way, they said. *Sadness, pain, labour — always.* But oh, the vanity of man! Surely a glorious destiny required some sacrifice?

And all around the innocent creatures died, by pestilence, disease or misplaced trust. They cried, they screamed, they wept.

But the ears of Heaven were stopped up. His sleep was as deaf as the night. His dream was a silent cage, a silent circle. He trod the edges of the cage, he walked the silent circle, repeating and repeating the same scenes, seeing none of it through. A girl would sit upon his shoulder and sing. Red eyes she had like rubies, red as a red moon, too red to look at for long.

And red needed no spokesman.
Red spoke for itself. In silence, to a deaf ear.

The scribe hears no voice dictating. His hand must nonetheless move. So history writes itself, out of control, a mad scribbling, meaningless, tragic.

Here is my curse upon the Dry Land, she cried, *that all the creatures shall forget their words, lost for the calls that make them one nation. Your cries shall be only mad rage and fear, no sense nor ideas in them. You beasts shall lose your art of speech, and with it all your harmony. For food the strong shall take the weak, and the small in their turn shall undermine the great by a base and subtle strategy.*

And so the animals changed, each according to its fear, each according to its need. In tooth and claw they

changed, in fang and horn and hoof. Sabres and knives were in their mouths and pikes and bludgeons on their heads. The fur became a coat of mail, the shell a bailey wall.

Fear. Pain. Death. All nature was at war.

And here is my curse upon man, she said, *that all men shall lose their tongues, lost for the words that make them brothers. This one commonwealth I shall divide into a hundred nation-states, and your nations themselves shall be sundered many times. In tribes and in clans you shall be set apart, one fraction from another, and neither by the word of your mouth nor by the words in your books shall you speak as one nation to its neighbour.*

So from that day forward each man was loyal to his own kingdom and to no other, because no man could understand any more the speech of other Kingdoms. The Dry Land was divided, each part of it walled off against the rest.

The fur became a coat of mail, the shell a bailey wall. All nature was at war.

23 MARCH

WAR

Dispute over territory. The forests destroyed. The Subtle State.

And she whispered to the nations, saying secretly to each: *See, your neighbour has more land than you, has better land, has richer land. Take what is due to you. For I stand with you. Get me what is mine.*

The same words in many tongues. The same voice speaking in the brain. Then silently, to herself alone: *I am queen of you all. By your folly shall I rule you, even to the last whimper.*

He is mine, said the red moon rising.

There was wine in the cask, red wine in the cup.

But only blood in the mouth.

So that was how the wars began, by the division of men into kingdoms and by the loss of the common speech. And the wars lasted for a thousand years.

The nations fell upon their neighbours. Consumed or were consumed. Devoured or were devoured. Furtive breakfasting of slime in a cess-pool, futile couplings unworthy of record. Yet those histories were written nonetheless, each state the jealous guardian of its own vain journals. Much heraldry was there, much standard-bearing pomp, much trumpeting of blind loyalties, much painting and re-painting of maps. So much was common sense smothered by patriotism, vanity, misguided idealism and petty tragedies, that the greater tragedy went all but unnoticed.

For the wars did not destroy only men, their machines, their cities. It was the land itself that bore the gravest wounds, for it was a delicate abundance, a fragile scheme of things. Wanton disorder was only a mask.

The forest died, and none knew why; the grass bled, and no man could tell from what injury. The rivers choked with dead and dying fish; but why the fish died remained a mystery forever.

Without a tree I cannot live, cried the man who remembered the green forests. The ale-houses swayed with a sad gaiety.

And the children wept for no good reason.

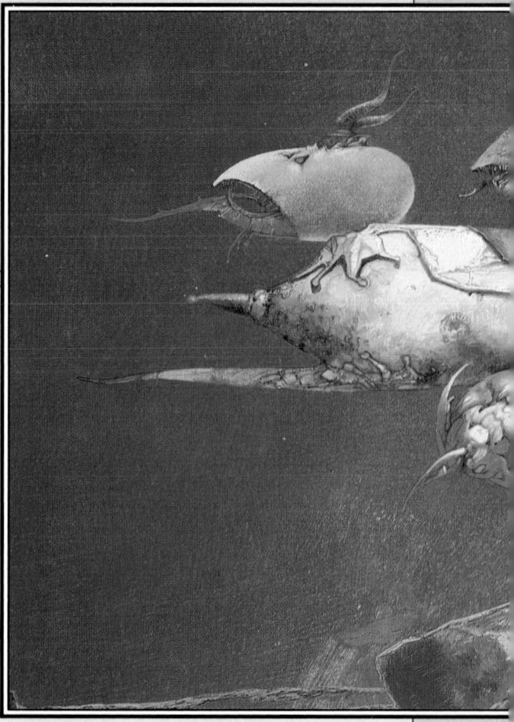

The nations fell upon their neighbours. Consumed or were consumed. Devoured or were devoured.

Much heraldry was there,
much standard-bearing pomp…

...much trumpeting of blind loyalties,
much painting and re-painting of maps.

There is a thin chain that binds us all, the mouse to the crow, the snail to the rabbit, the husbandman even to his vermin. And the thin chain broke in every link.

There is a stairway from basement to attic, a spiral mystery that makes us one household, the trout and the raven, the cricket and the ram; and even the swallow in the eaves is brother to the spider in the vault. And the stairway broke in every tread.

And did they need a stairway, the creatures of the dark? Her Subtle State may shit on every floor, may piss through any wall. We died. We died. By arrow, dagger, lance and spear. By bullet, poison-gas and bomb. Who can say how we died? Who can count the ways? This is not history. Write it not.

When the eye is wet, may the pen be dry.

And the hidden art was a lost art, that every piece of skin and every smallest hair should know its own shape and have a memory of its purpose. No creature is described from outside, and now the inner book itself was torn.

So the children died from strange distortions, too many heads, too many legs, too few eyes, not enough skin. They were born without teeth and died unweened. They were born without mouths and died unsuckled. They were born without blood and died unborn.

For a thousand years there was only war. War and disease. War and decay. War and despair. Till every state but one had fallen.

So the Subtle State had no city walls, being the last kingdom on all the Dry Land. And all the forests belonged to the Subtle State, though every tree was dead. And all the rich pastures were hers, though not a blade of grass survived.

The Dry Land was at peace at last. The desert was at peace. No bombs, no gun-fire, no sirens wailing from the towers. The planes rotted, the mortars crumbled to dust. Silence even in the dark night.

Yet still the children wept for no good reason.
This is not history. May the pen be dry.

No corn, no seed. No fields of corn. No bread.

Only in the sea and in the sky was food for the Subtle State. So they trapped the song-bird with lime upon the window-ledge, and made an enemy even of the trusting sparrow. They baked the docile turtles that walked above the tide, and they boiled even the merry fishes for their food.

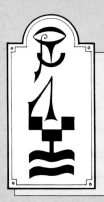

24 DE PROFUNDIS

THE DEATH OF THE SEA

The floating cities are sacked. The whales and Glass are destroyed.

And so it was that the sea was destroyed. Wrong piled upon wrong.

Behold the sea, cried the forgotten bride of man. *See, how Glass your brother boasts in his proud wealth. See how the people of the sea have forgotten you. This meagre land is a poor heritage for man. The ocean instead shall be yours. For I stand with you. Get me what is mine.*

And even the few men that were left were enough. Enough to lay waste the cities of the sea, enough to put all their friendly people to the sword. The fleets were stolen, plundered, and what they could not use they burned. The palaces were rifled, despoiled, the libraries scuttled with all their books intact. So the wisdom of the sea-people passed away, and all their great history rotted with their noble books. Blind beacons marked the way to nowhere on the ocean floor.

The beacon is trumped by the snuffing-hood.
Black blood. She is the thief of light.

The Dry Land was at peace at last. The desert was at peace.

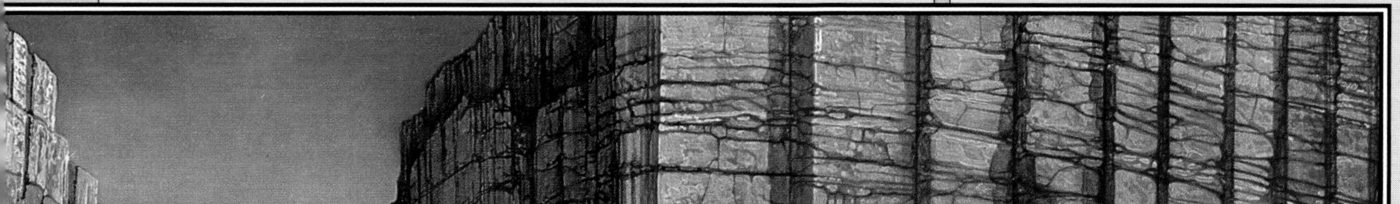

And then it was another one's turn to die. For meat, for sport, for naked Malice's sake.

I look in at the eye of the giant, said Malice, *for his eye is the window of a room. And inside is an old, old man, seated in an ancient study, full of wisdom, yet no older than today. Why should this be?*

And the men slaughtered the whales, and they kept them in pens like frightened cattle for their food, and those they could not catch they killed with poisoned bait and barbéd hook, with wire noose and explosive shells. And the wisest creatures on all the Earth queued up to die, impatient for the end.

Put out my eyes, said the old, old man, *that I see not my own children die.*

Kill me now, said the last whale, *for I cannot kill myself.*

The beacon is trumped by the snuffing-hood.
Wisdom by Malice. Innocence by Hatred.

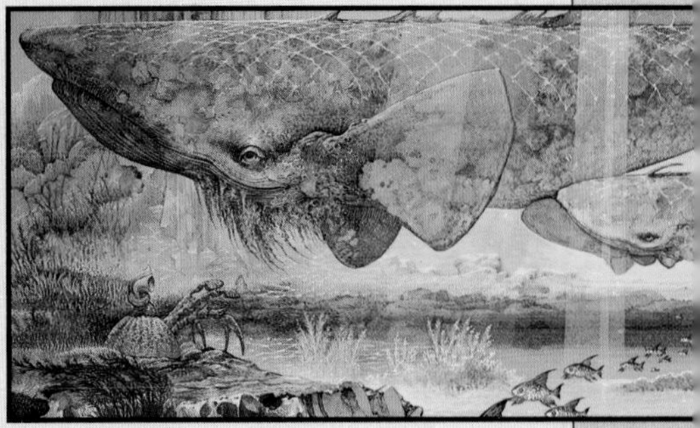

"Kill me now," said the last whale, "for I cannot kill myself."

His palace stood on the shore, clean, empty.

But what of Glass himself? And what of the wife of Glass? They had no word for malice, no word for horror, no word for decay. Glass walked on the hog-backed hills, the dead hills, the dead countryside. And some there were that floated, their corpses swollen with foul gases. Then slowly they sank and came to rest upon the ocean floor, hog-backed hills of slime, dead hills of rotting filth, a dead landscape of empty eyes, weed-covered bones.

And he came upon his wife in the hills of bone, and what should he find but a dead hand and a clouded eye? No smile upon her lips. No answer to his kiss. So Glass must learn a new word.

And the new word was grief.

From mouth to mouth the message passed. *This is disease,* whispered the dead mouth. *My recipe for corruption. Here is how.*

So Glass must learn his last word.

And the last word was Death.

His palace stood upon the shore, clean, empty. The three horns silenced forever. His kingdom had passed away.

He is mine, said the red moon to the red sky.

He is mine, said Malice to the dead sea.

25 ELEGY

THE DEATH OF THE AIR

The birds are killed. The rainbow is broken. Beltempest is destroyed.

No fish, no crabs, no whale-meat for the children of man. Only in the air did meat remain for the Subtle State.

Behold the head of the locust, said Malice. *It has a thousand eyes. The locust sees me coming in a thousand different poses, and yet I pluck it from the air like defenceless fruit.*

So the people of the air, the merry birds that roosted on the wing, even the gentle urchins of the sky — they were fair game, easy prey. And the men shot them down for sport, and those they could not reach with arrows, they deceived with traps and nets. Some they kept in cages for fresh meat, trembling, weeping, fairy babies slaughtered for their flesh. And the prettiest children on all the Earth cried out for death, impatient for the end.

Put out my thousand eyes, said the locust, *for I cannot watch a thousand locusts die.*

Kill me now, said the last fairy, *for I cannot kill myself.*

The rainbow broke in the sky.

No rain, no hail, no snow. The long-dead forests burned in root and branch, the last snail baked within his house, and even the buried worm was cooked beneath the ground. The long-dead rivers were scorched away, their dried courses like crazéd pavements to the sea.

Where are your flocks? cried Malice to the good shepherd, for all his clouds had gone astray. *Your bow is broken in the sky. Storm, wind, the bell, the bleating clouds. Your kingdom is dead from end to end. Beltempest, sleep forever.*

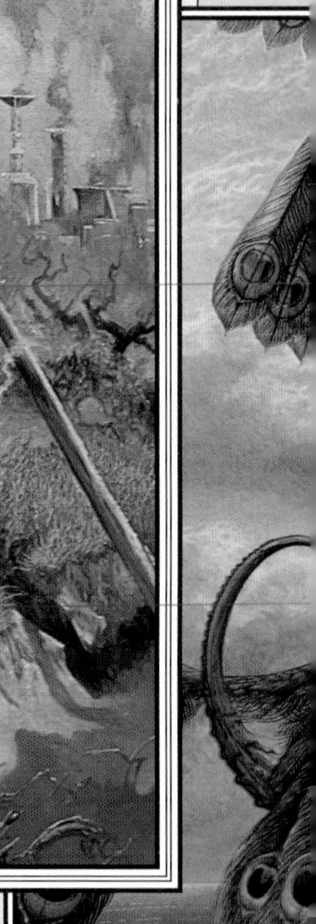

And the prettiest children on all the Earth
cried out for death, impatient for the end.

He had come forth like a beast, mighty and proud, yet he died like a child, weeping. And with him his wife and every kind of flying beast save one.

Gone was the song of the trumpet, the tolling bell. Gone was every music from the Earth save one. For in the high air the mothers of man still called upon the flute. And they came down to the city to die, impatient for the end.

Pluck out my feathers, said the mothers of man, for the eyes on my wings have seen enough.

Kill me now, said the last to die, for I cannot kill myself.

26 CURFEW

THE LAST CITY

The city is closed up. The rule of law. The dream goes on.

So the sea was like dull lead, heavy and still. Unfit to drink. Even the air itself had lost its breath. The Dry Land was desert from cape to cape, the dunes motionless now, the rock cold and naked, and nowhere but in the last city was any living thing left alive.

Like a huge, lonely house, the last city was covered by a single roof, its doors shut tight against the world, its windows shuttered, sealed against the light and the smoke. For only in the closed city was there breathable air, drinkable water.

No man inside dared look out at the red sky.
No man was left outside to look in upon the city.

And the last city was poor. It was degraded and cruel, a place of weariness and squalor. Such food as they could grow was hard to come by, and each man must earn his crust by hard work or trickery. The tainted water was bought and sold by the measure like liquid silver. Even the very air was rationed, earned, shared out, so much to this man, so much to that man. For the water and the air that were in the city were all they had, and must be collected and cleaned like daily laundry.

The city was huge, covering the space of a thousand farms, yet every last inch was planned and kept to account. Nothing kept its place without fighting for its place, a ruthless law which also governed all its people. The sick and the old were put to death, their bodies' substance returned for the common nourishment. The simple-minded were put down. The rebel was shot. The poet paid with his life for public complaint.

But most of all the women died. A fertile womb may have many mouths. We could not afford mothers, for we could not afford children. How many women survived no one knows. Sufficient, it would seem, to keep the game alive, to be sure that the Subtle State itself survived. Both males and females were used like cattle, herded, spayed, castrated, slaughtered. Their own brothers bore the cattle-prods. And the butcher's mistress licked her crimson lips and smiled.

She walked only in the veins of men, and her only throne was in their heads.

And did they see her smile? Did she walk the streets like a blood-stained whore? Did she sit on a throne of gold to make her decree?

No. More subtle was the Subtle State than that. Her feet had no need of pavements to walk upon, and she sat on no throne of gold. She walked only in the veins of men, and her only throne was in their heads. Her decree made no sound but in the ear of him who must carry it out.

Take your brother for your wife, she said, *for your brother has no womb. And the children shall be your pleasure till they bleed. And if any man stand in your way, then kill him, for life is the cheapest thing we have.*

And nowhere but in that one city was anything left alive on all the Earth.

In the measureless void the child slept on, dreaming among his dream-toys. Both young and old he was, even as a mortal man is both young and old, always dreaming a dream or remembering a dream. The living of it is always somehow out of reach. Over and over he played the game, a closed circle, a wheel of pursuit. And he never tired of it.

He was running in the wood, the hunter strangely pursued by his own quarry, a ghost chasing a ghost. The leaves before him chattered like a wave; the leaves behind him whispered like surf.

She hid herself in a sparrow's nest, and he heard her many-throated voice. He saw her running thighs, but held only the slim branches of an ash. She fled to a hollow tree, and he heard her stifled laughter. But when he got to the tree she was gone.

Only a bees' honeycomb remained, and the hollow tree hummed like an organ-loft.

And the rest of the story you know, though it must nonetheless be re-told, by you to your children, and by your children to theirs.

Lest we forget what we were and what we threw away.

27 FUGUE

EXILE

The fleet leaves. The seven moons plundered. Deep space.

The city was empty. Her halls were silent and still. Poisoned air came and went like an invisible guest. Dead brine trespassed in her streets unchallenged.

In the north of the city her mighty doors stood open. Open not to the land that lay all around like a cemetery, but open like poke-lids, open to the innocent sky. Pillars of fire were the last things that burned on all the Earth. A thousand ships were the last things that moved.

The Subtle State had fled to the first of the seven moons.

Who can tell how we fare? For there is no chronicle but the barest truth, that every moon we tread upon is plundered and laid waste. From stone to stone we cross the great waters of Heaven, and every stepping-stone is destroyed. There is none to follow us, and no one shall.

The fleet grows like an army in rich territory, fattened by crops it has not sown, plundering town after town, moon after moon.

And when six of the moons were dead, their skins sucked out like dry fruit, only Darkness remained, hiding in the shadow of the long-dead Earth. The fleet clustered around it like fire-flies. And so at last there was light upon Darkness, but only the baleful glimmer of plunder. And the black moon was sliced and devoured like a black cheese, dissected and used up like the varied pieces of a tree, the trunk for the walls and the timbers in the roof, the twigs for kindling and the branches for the fuel.

So the fleet stood on the edge of the void itself. A flock of black crows gazed out across the fields of space, and everywhere they looked were jewels, gold pieces, silver rings and trinkets.

This treasure is ours, said the small voice in the brain, for the riches we were given are all used up. We shall take it all. For I stand with you. Get me what is mine.

So the giant fleet moved away from the Sun, and the long-dead Earth and all her dead moons tumbled away like dull marbles.

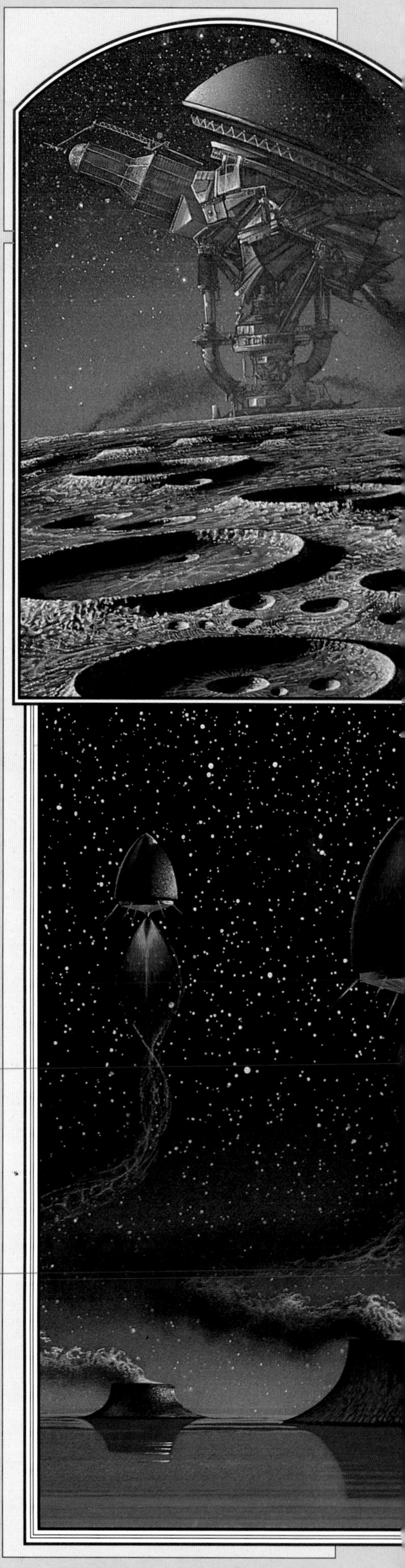

What use is but one Sun, said the small voice, *when we can choose from a billion? What use is but one dead Earth, when she has sisters beyond counting?*

The pen refuses to write. Even the ink will not quit the well.

This is not history. Yet it must be written.

Lest we forget what we were and what we threw away.

And that is how we came to dwell in space itself, a homeless people searching for a home, yet forced to make a home in what we had. For ten thousand years the ships looked for a harbour. The flock of black crows flew. Over black fields. Seeking distant treasure. For ten thousand years a swarm of bees had no hollow tree, no place for the honeycomb.

The queen lay in her cell, and her cell hummed like an organ-loft.

From stone to stone we cross the great waters of Heaven, and every stepping-stone is destroyed.

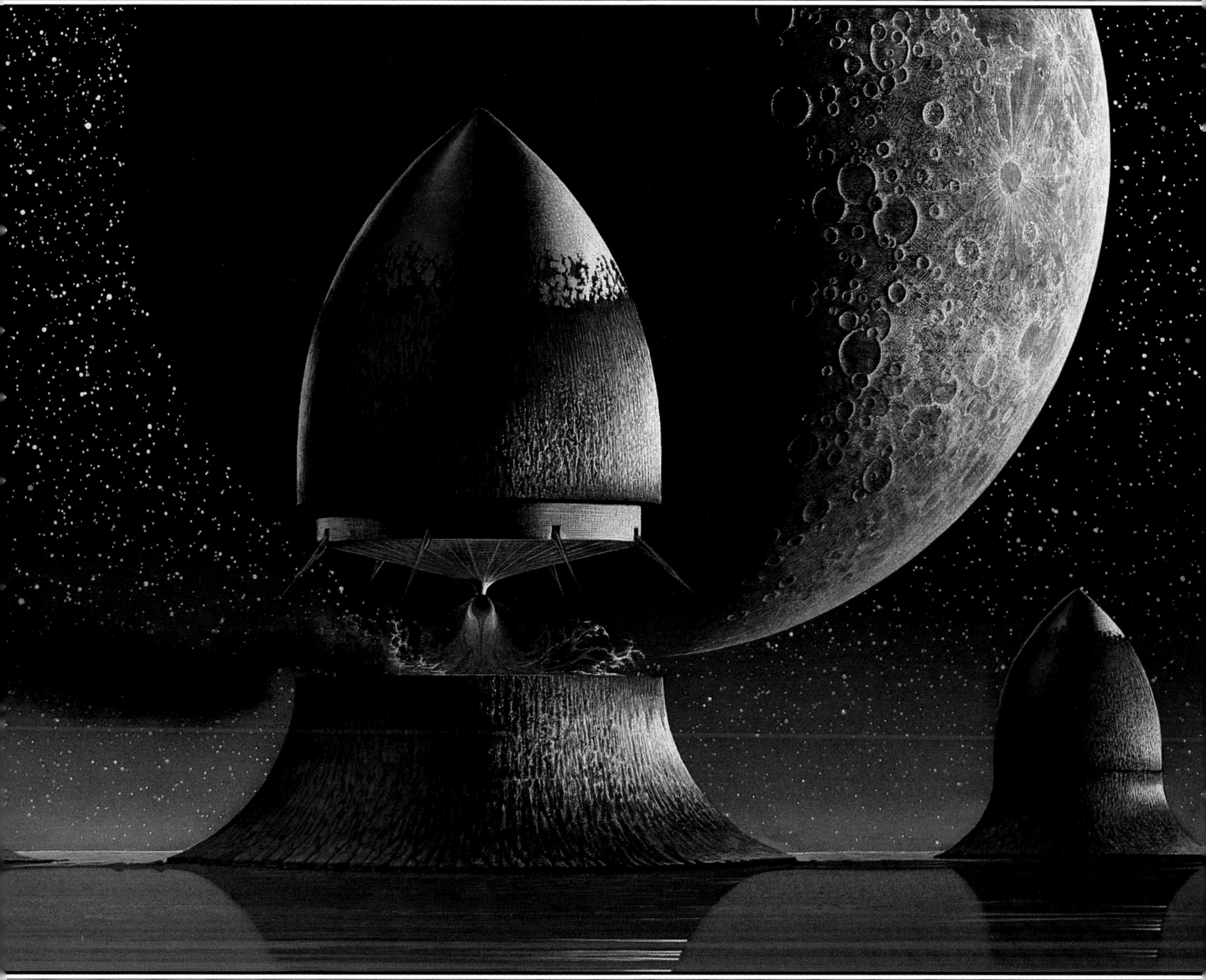

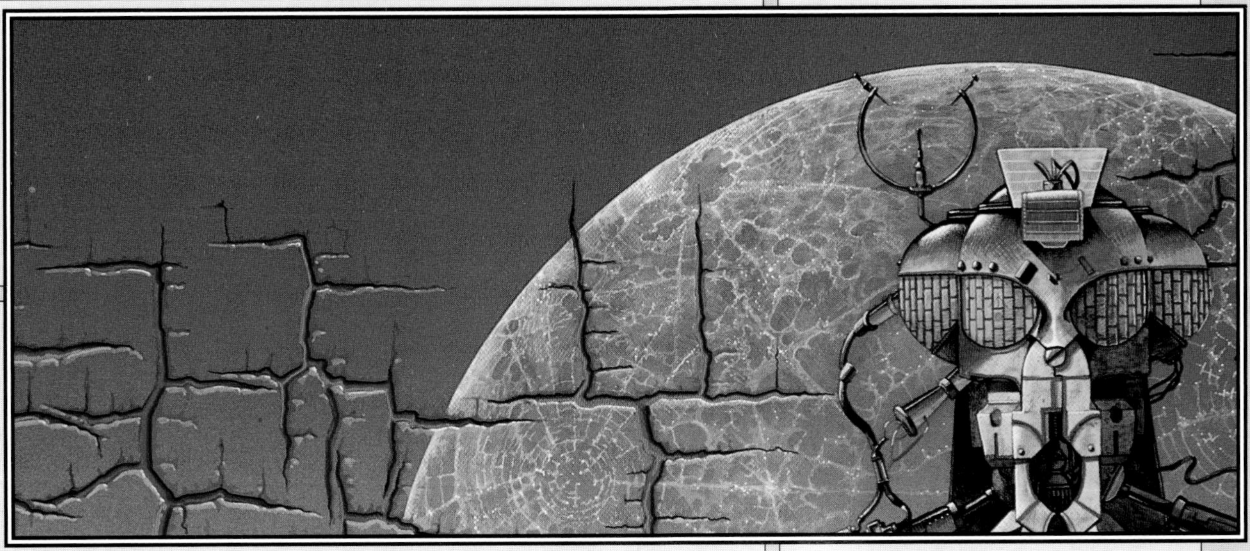

And Heaven's jewelry glistened all around, each star a pin-point of day-light in a vast black sphere. The stars behind us moved away, reddened by flight, yet those before us came no closer. For the black sphere seemed to grow like a slowly inflating ball. There was nowhere to go. Everywhere moved away from us. We could not go back. We were already nowhere.

The fleet panicked through space like a flock of starving birds in a blizzard, yet seemed to hang suspended, motionless. For all its haste, it seemed to sleep. For all its anguish, it seemed at peace. The stars, like fleeing spiderlings, were never caught. Grew dimmer every hundred years.

So what of man? And what of this New Earth? The sleeper dreamed, and all his creatures stood upon his awakening, courtiers around the bed of the king, waiting for justice, waiting for reproach. For could it be that even man might be forgot, and all his wantonness go unrepaired?

The clock ticked. The clock ticked.

And the children of the children's children passed away, life after meaningless life, name after meaningless name, a ceaseless repetition, a procession of lists. Lists do not make history. Yet history must be written.

Lest we forget what we were and what we threw away.

"What use is but one Sun, when we can choose from a billion?"

28 MISERERE

A NEW ORDER

Lost in the void. Remorse in adversity. Malice fades away.

Thus was anger spent and come to nothing, for no axe may strike against thin air.

And here is how the kingdom changed and all men in it.

Alone together in the void, fellow-travellers to nowhere, they shared a common terror, common grief, common loneliness. And even the secret voice of malice and hatred softened to a cry of pity and shame.

Oh, my little ones! she wept. *What have I done to my people? Your home is destroyed, and we are alone. Nowhere to go. No riches for us in all the fading glory of Heaven.*

And a new order came to be. The cruel passed away, and the children of the cruel were gentle and kind. The burning tiger was devoured by his own flame, and the child of the tiger had neither claws nor fangs, nor yet the proud roar of its father. Soft feathers only, a simple, humble mind, and a voice like Summer afternoons.

So the centuries passed. Like frightened children the people clung to one another for warmth and consolation, and the voice in the ear became like the voice of a mother, soft, comforting. Like feathers with eyes. Like green triumphant. The sound of golden flutes across the long-forgotten, long-dead seas.

There was no red sky here. No red moon. Red was a memory.

And so the golden age was told, told and re-told. Chapters of green. Parables of green. Yet green needs no evangelist.

Green shall learn its own lesson.

She slept, escaping from truth and guilt.

And she dreamed, papering the walls of her mind with visions. She ran through a wood naked, young and naked in a wood of sweet-smelling ferns. The dew sparkled on her skin like dancing beads. The twigs snapped beneath her feet. Little birds flew from their nests above her, whistling and chirruping in happy alarm.

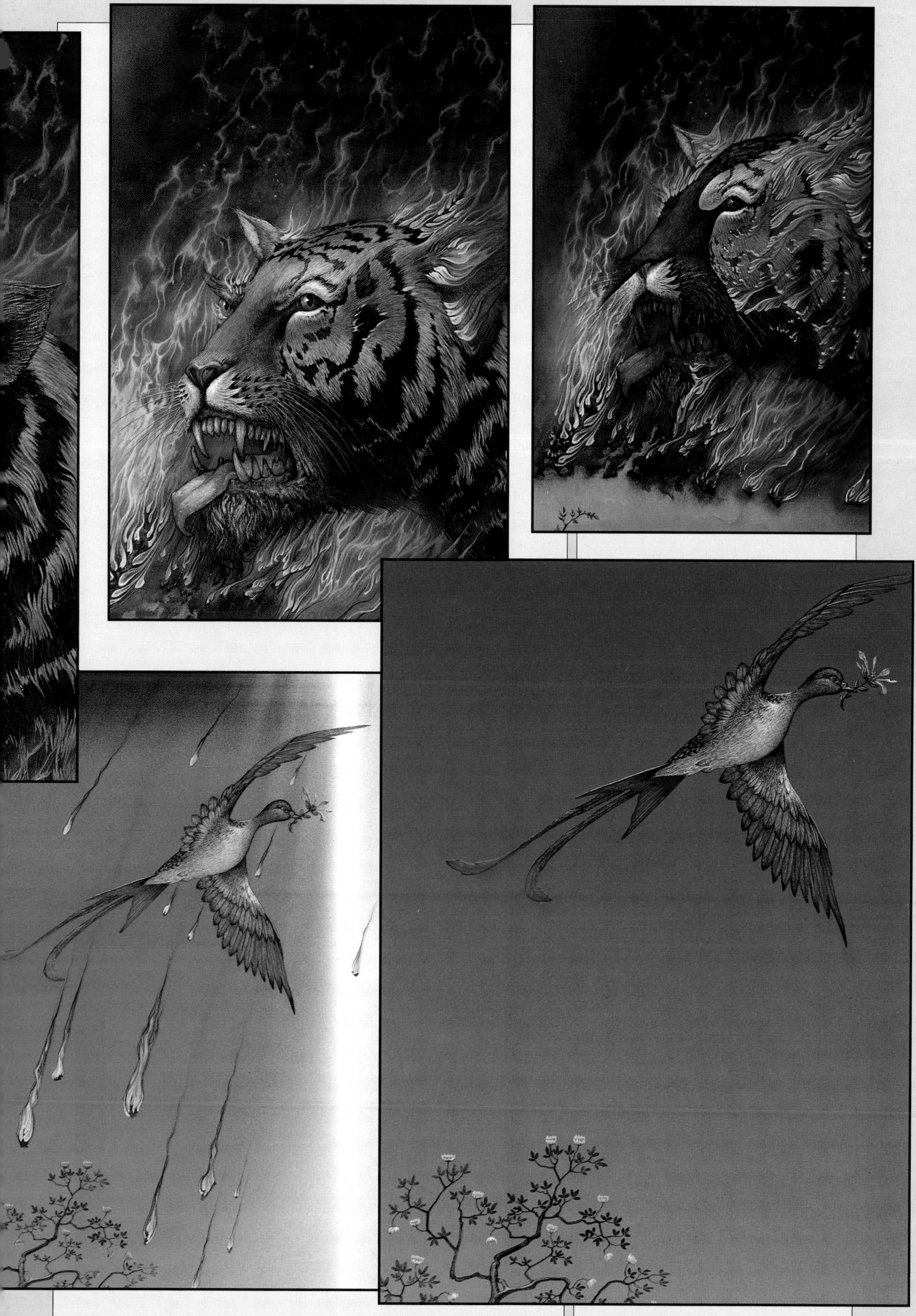

"What dream-world is this?" she cried, for she knew that all the woods were dead.

What dream-world is this? she cried, for she knew that all the woods were dead.

May I never wake! she sobbed, for she knew that there were no ferns, no dew, no snapping twigs, no singing birds. All that was gone, dead, burned away like words on a page. And she hid in the hollow dream-tree, sobbing.

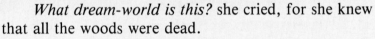

The engines buzzed like monstrous bees. Her cell hummed like an organ-loft.

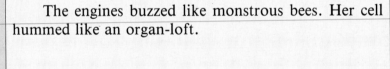

29 ANTHEM

ONE DREAM FOR TWO

In the wood. The satyr catches the nymph. Endless exile.

And here is how the story almost ends, the place where the penitent is shriven, and wrong is put to right.

For somewhere in time and space there is a wood. The trees are as old as time itself, yet never die. There is no Autumn, no Spring. The leaves are always green, the ferns forever fresh and smelling of promised love. The wood *is* a wood, yet not a wood. The wood *is* a dream, yet not a dream. Impossible. Yet, given the right words, it must be so.

There is a child running... No, it is a man who runs. No, he does not run. He flies like a giant bird. There are horns on the top of his head; his head is both young and old. A tail as long as a cloud, golden, many-coloured. Painted like a rainbow.

The leaves before him chatter like a wave, the leaves behind him whisper like surf. Who is chasing whom? Does the wind chase the wind? Does the fish pursue the tail, or the tail pursue the fish?

He looks in a sparrow's nest. Four red throats scream for food.

What deer is this that runs on but two legs? Not a deer but a nymph, with legs as smooth to touch as peach-skin or the petals of a rose. He comes at last to a hollow tree. Stifled laughter — or is it sobbing? — from within.

The wood is a wood, yet not a wood. The wood is a dream, yet not a dream.

For the wind has caught the wind!
The fish has caught the fish's tail!

The satyr reaches in. Warm flesh, soft, yielding. The nymph is as naked as a pillow. There is a buzzing like monstrous bees. The hollow tree hums like an organ-loft.

For the wind has caught the wind!
The fish has caught the fish's tail!

The dream was in the cask. He turned the tap, but *she* held the cup. Not wine, but *honey* on their lips!

Red eyes she has, red enough to look at forever!
And red lips shall have no spokesman.
For red lips can speak for themselves.

So the dream ends, swallows itself up in truth. And all the children shout to the king: *joy, love, peace!* And the crier walks the city calling: *Oyez! Oyez! The king is wed! Long live the king!*

For all the trumps are trumped by Love.

And so the fleet flew on, fuelled of itself, propelled by its own destiny. A honeycomb of cells. A honeycomb of destinies. But one cell was empty, a shrine to sweetness come from sour, to the Love that makes a family of us all, and all men brothers.

The generations came and went, name after name. But now with pride and a purpose, now with a firm and noble resolve. History remained only a list of names, but there is glory even to the nameless, when virtue, honour and humility are their accompaniment. And virtue needs no payment.

For virtue shall pay for itself.

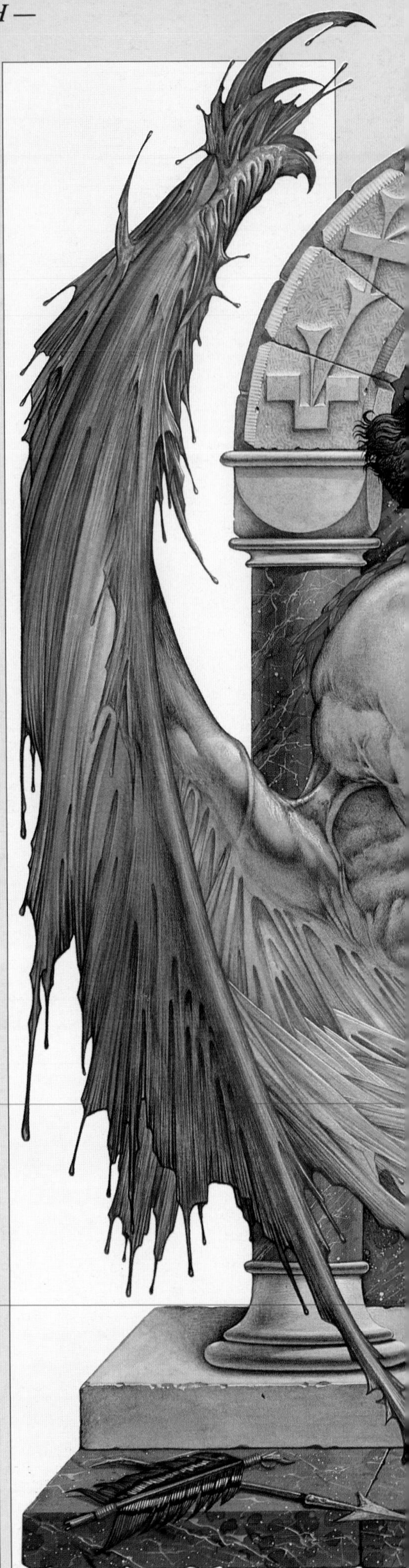

30 PROCESSIONAL

FALSE ARRIVALS

The stars are found again. The search for a New Earth.

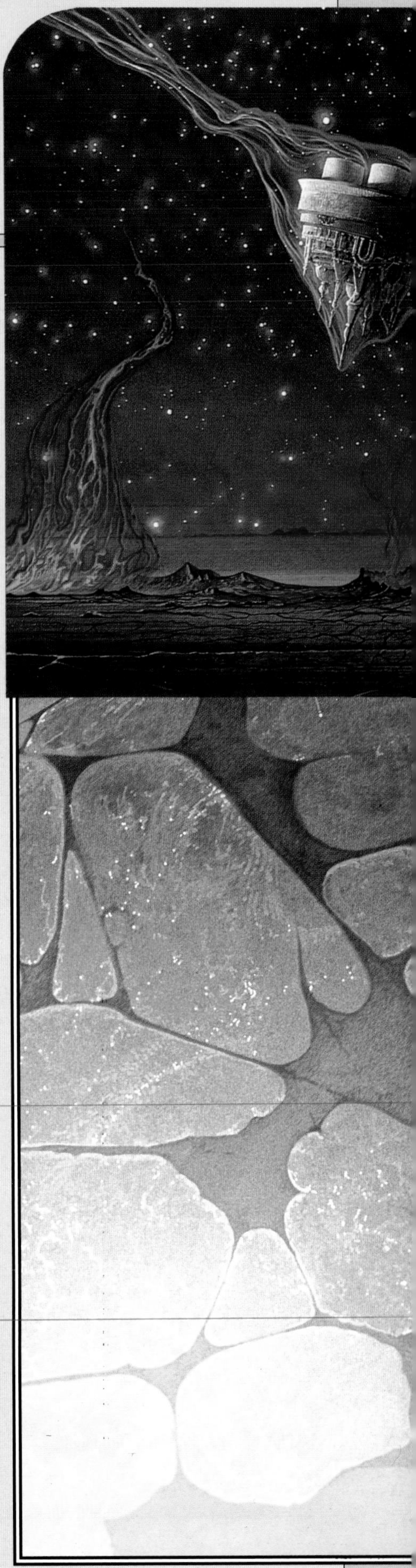

The generations came and went, name after name.

Woman side by side with man, holding hands, fresh as on the first day, each generation nobler than the last. And so they raised their little children, meek and selfless in society, yet strong and resolute when times demanded sacrifice.

And so we came at last to the stars, for the void seemed fuller and brighter than ever before. The heavens sang, or seemed to sing, with colour. Light burst all around us like flames in a burning forest. Yet this was no consuming fire. Such flames do not destroy. This was the heat of new suns, life-giving, glorious daylight. And all around our fleet, like a great wheel, there turned a huge rainbow, clean, unbroken. Colours as beautiful as mighty music. And the music sang even in our hearts like a lullaby.

You are home, said the rainbow. *Here is my everlasting promise. You have come to your own place and shall never leave it.*

So we came at last to our own, but not without Pain.

I must stay with you, said Pain. *For only in your long exile did you learn to love and care for one another, and it is compassion that binds you each to each. But do not fear me. I shall be merciful.*

So we came at last to our own, but not without Death.

I may not leave you, said Death, *for only by me can weariness be cured and a pathway be cleared for the new. But do not be afraid, for I am only forgetfulness. I am a kind illusion. I shall be as gentle in a clockwork world as I may be.*

We came at last to the stars, but let no man believe that we were home and safe. The universe is filled with the splendour of a billion billion suns. Suns are common stuff, like grains of sand upon a beach. But who can show you a grain of sand that has its own invisible family of dust?

Even planets are common stuff, though hard to find.

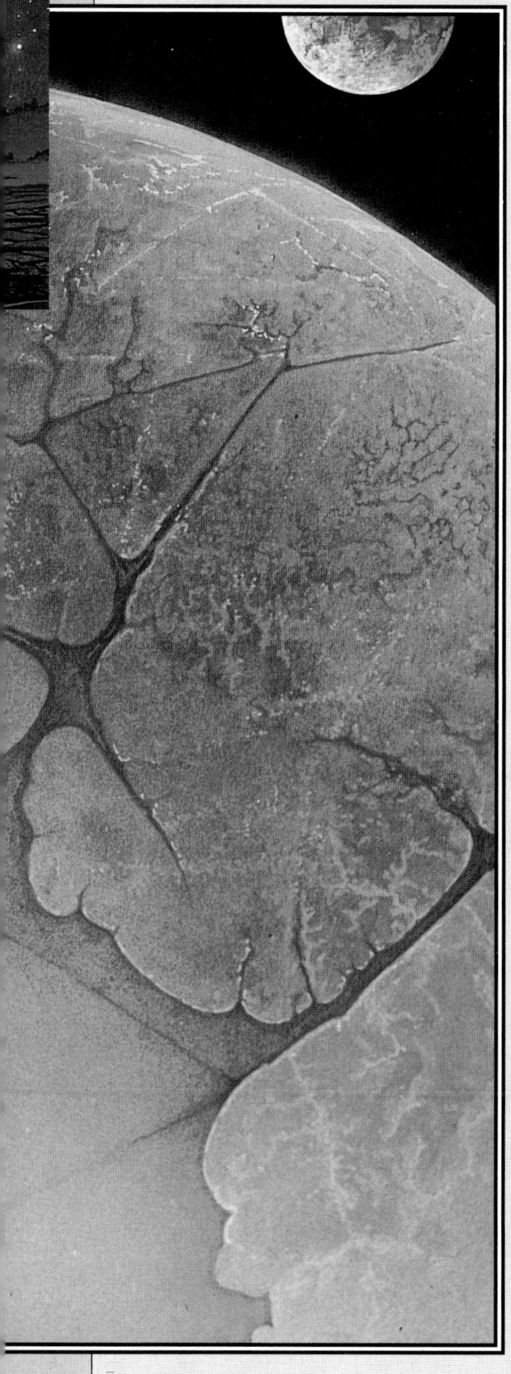

So we searched the rich jewel-box of Heaven, hopeful still, though many generations died still hoping. And the generations told the old tales of long, long ago. Stories only half-believed, of meadows, yellow flowers, trees and friendly beasts.

Our fleet was like a hundred thousand cities. Towns within towns. Harbours within harbours. Ships within ships.

Who can count the ships we lost? Who can count the men? For even planets are common stuff, though hard to find. But none there was that boasted either air or water, least of all a flower or a beast.

Our ships went down burning, and no one heard their mute despair.

Our ships went down drowning, never seen again.

Each new world had a new way of killing men, be it quickly by fire, or more slowly by cold or poison gas. But the best worlds were the cruellest, for only after years of hope and hard work did they betray us, by disease, by earthquake, by volcano.

Those worlds are listed, even as the despairing generations are listed. They have names, numbers, repetitions of sad statistics.

Numbers make poor history.

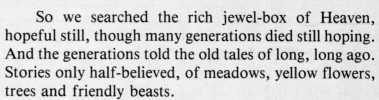

31 DA CAPO

THE NEW EARTH

Its creatures. The air, the water and the Second Sun. The new order.

And the rest of the story you know, though it must be told again. We are here, in this impossible place, happy and at home. The New Earth is blue, blue as the eye of a baby, too blue to be true. It is a balm to the soul. Even the sky makes us weep for joy.

So our great cities came down, guided by their scout-ships. Slowly they fell, like trays of delicate crockery. And some came to rest upon the sands, and some were in the grasslands, and some settled upon the very ocean itself. A thousand? A hundred thousand cities? We did not count them, nor the people within, nor the number of our pretty children. We counted only as far as one:

One Earth.
One People.
One World.

The first day of a new history.

And only one moon in the first night, as bright as a silver coin. And we called the new moon Light, in remembrance of Darkness.

Lest we forget what we were and what we threw away.

Do any eyes see us come, apart from the birds and beasts? Does a new Beltempest guide us through the new clouds? Does a second Glass welcome us to the second sea?

Who can say? For this New Earth is subtle. Her ways are not our ways. She must be wooed like an exotic bride, a foreign princess. We must learn her mysterious language: not she ours. For this New Earth was not given to man, was not made for him. We are, and always shall be, guests.

So our cities stood, safe and sound upon the New Earth, and on the morning of the second day we were visited by the gentle creatures of the air, fearless, full of endearing curiosity. And the cattle of the plains were all around, filling the air with their bellows and calls, watching, sniffing, licking the salt sweat from our arms, feeding from our very hands. No malice was there in their faces, only an inquisitive trust. Where a city had come down on the ocean, there all the fishes came to see, testing its shape with every sense they had. The

Slowly they fell, like trays of delicate crockery.

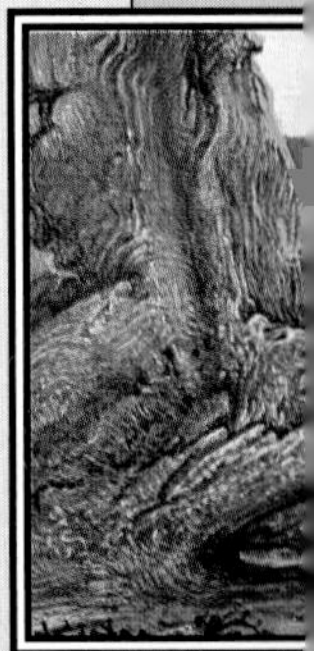

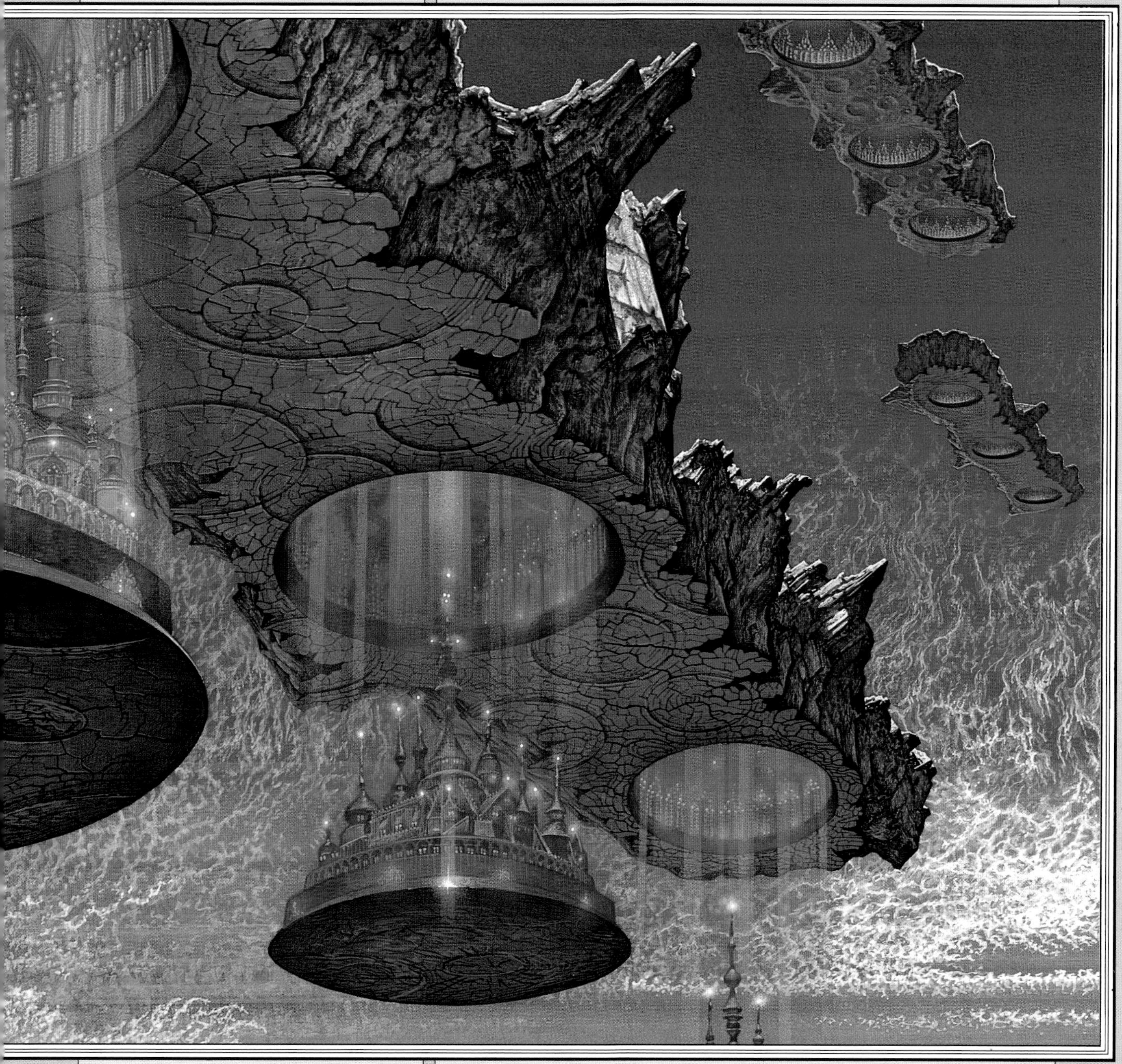

great whales lay all around in a wide circle, their innocent eyes bright with ancient wisdom. Their great jaws half-smiling.

And we cried to all the creatures of the New Earth, with great love in our hearts, with salt tears on our cheeks. For there were hairy beasts and scaly beasts, and some were small and others large, and some lived in the forests and others in the grassland, each to his own place and to his given food. And the garner never emptied, nor yet brimmed over.

Not one of you shall flee, said man, *nor hide from me. I am not to be feared, for this is your kingdom. Side by side we shall walk, and all our pursuit is play.*

Can any man describe fresh air, when even his

grandfather's grandfather never knew it? What is it like to breathe for the first time, air that did not taste of metal, rubber, vaguely tainted by sewage or death?

And who could describe a river or the sea, when all the water he ever knew was his own re-cycled urine and sweat?

The Second Earth was beyond words, a feast for the senses, blinding, intoxicating. Men who had never had space enough in all their lives to run the length of a room, now trotted weakly through wide, scented pastures. Women who had never disposed of water enough in all their lives even to rinse their hair, now thrashed and wallowed like squealing fish, glistening in the shallows.

And what words for this mighty Second Sun? Or for the rainbow's bridge from ground to ground? We had only seen the New Sun through smoked glass till now, only shifting patterns in the eye, short memories of coloured discs. The Sun needs no priesthood.

Need any man tell you what is worshipful in light?

It shall stay like this forever. This is the new order.

That when anything shall be done for the benefit of all, that we know the consequences first as far as we may. And it shall be done slowly, with watchfulness.

That when a man shall do anything for himself, then he shall decide against it when the answer is yes to this question: *Would this rich New Earth be poorer, if all men did what I shall do?*

And that when a man shall do anything not for himself, then he shall decide for it when the answer is yes to this question: *Would this rich New Earth be richer still, if all men did what I shall do?*

Three rules to rule the world, if all men rule themselves by them, and do not stop to say: But what of my brother? He does not live by these, so why should I?

To rule the world, we must begin, not with our brother, but with ourselves.

And so the book ends.

The dream is told. The great wheel of time spins on. They sit upon its rim, embracing like young fish. There is a dream-ring on a dream-finger. Bells. Trumpets. Mighty music in the organ-loft of Heaven. The fanfare never ends. It is always the beginning, always the end.

Impossible. Yet it is so.

We have no words.

It is always the beginning, always the end.

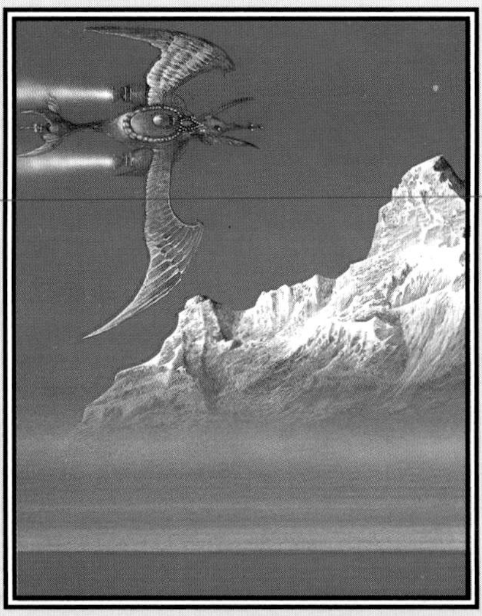

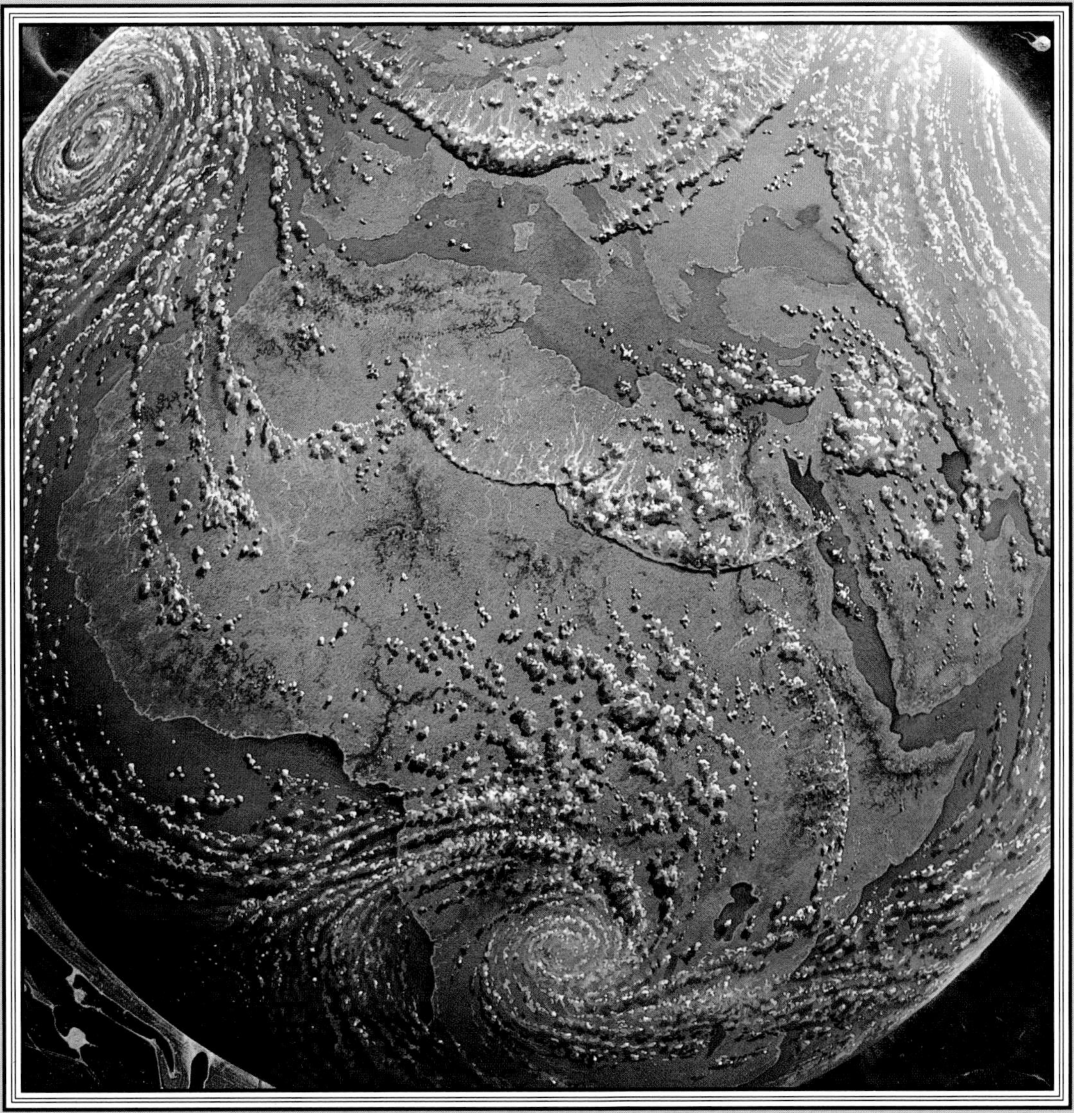

The Second Earth was beyond words,
a feast for the senses, blinding, intoxicating.

CODA

CODA

The message of Hermes.

The Coda, we now know, was engraved at a much later date, when Hermes was placed in orbit around Saturn, in our terms many thousands of years ago.

In this section we have decided to sacrifice style for literal accuracy, so that the interpretation may be observed with direct reference to the symbols. The words bracketed and in the italics are "understood" — that is, added by us for better understanding.

The numbers denote the separate verses or "cartouches".

1. And the children of the Earth came from Darkness and from the void to the blue world, (*which was*) the New Earth and the new home.

2. HERMES (*was only*) one of many ships, but HERMES (*was*) an exile of the New Earth because of the message and the book.

3. Because the children of the Earth must forget (*their*) origin, and not before the middle of youth rise up out of the New Earth, remembering nothing before the New Earth.

4. (*Then they*) fly to the great world of many rings of light, (*which shall be*) a beacon (*to them*) and a place to recall the history of (*their fore-*) fathers.

5. Because of the story of HERMES (*is*) a lantern of the past.

6. The five books (*tell*) the story of (*their fore-*) fathers and the story of the death of the First Earth.

7. The Second Earth (*is*) a child (*and*) must not die.

8. The oak and the fish, the snail and the spider, (*these are*) no lesser things than man.

9. The broken rainbow must (*be*) the (*whole*) rainbow.

10. The second arrow must strike (*its*) target.

11. But the Second Earth (*is*) like a man of metal (*and*) does not make (*its own*) destiny.

12. Man is not a man of metal.

13. Man makes the future of the Second Earth.

14. (*When*) man is the shepherd of the Second Earth, (*it will be*) the end of the childhood of man.

15. Man must not make war, but love and come together, just as the child of the void and the forgotten bride of man must love.

Cartouches 16 and 17 are reproduced again at the end of this edition. The interpretation of this final message is left to the reader.

Man makes the future of the Second Earth.

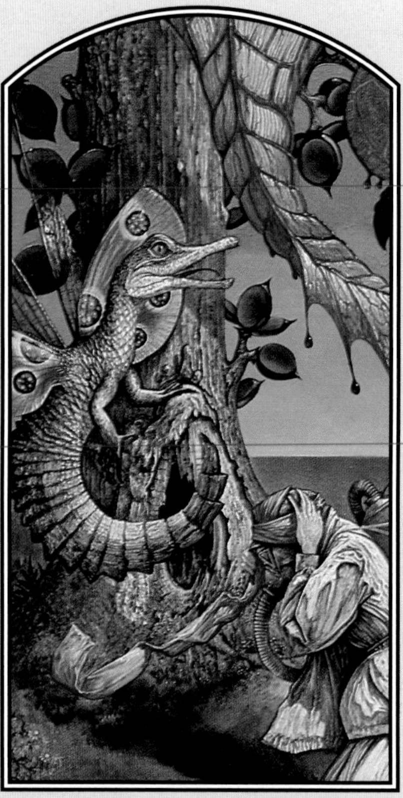

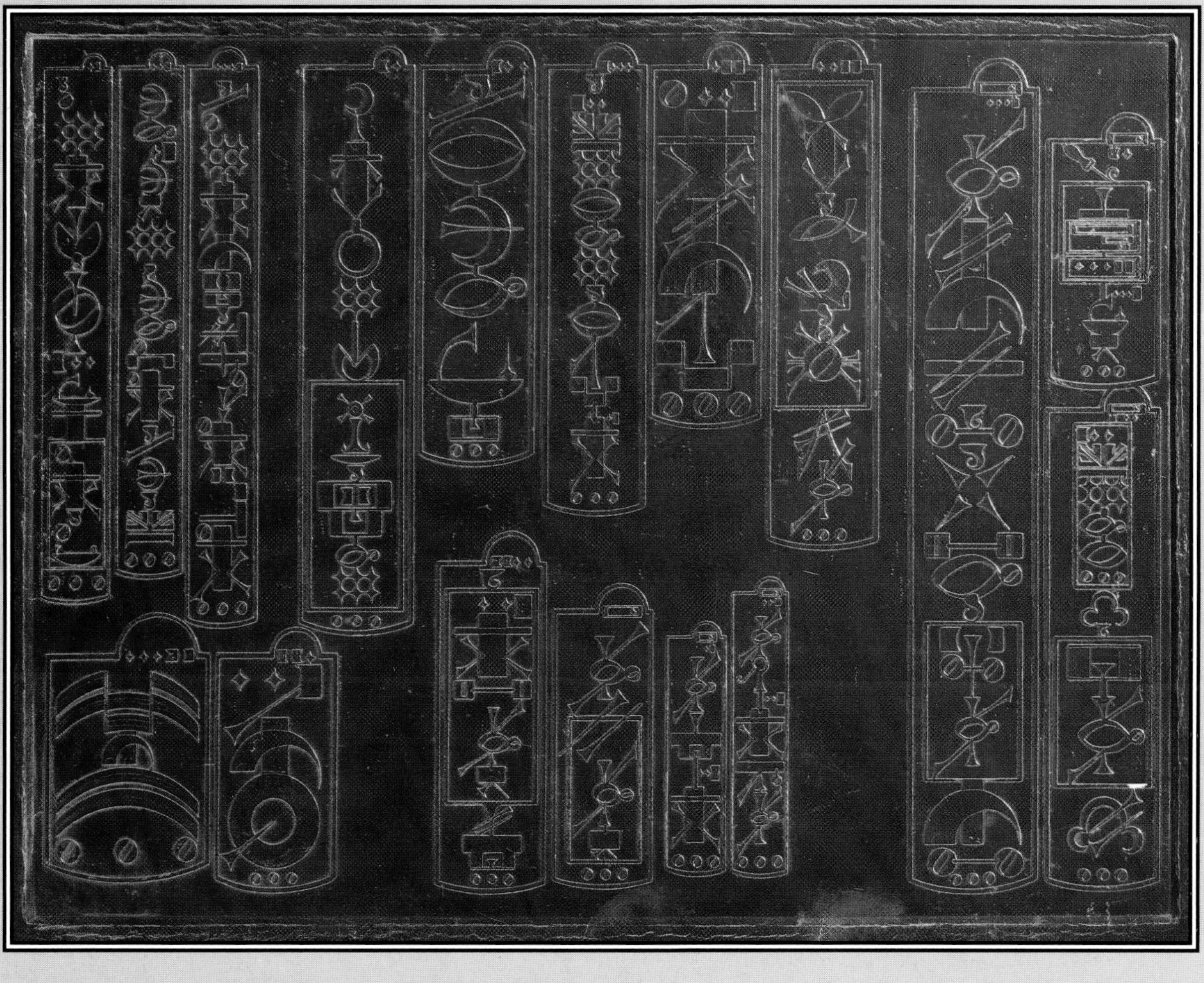

APPENDIX A

A SHORT IDEOGRAPHIC "GLOSSARY"

Celia Hiroshige

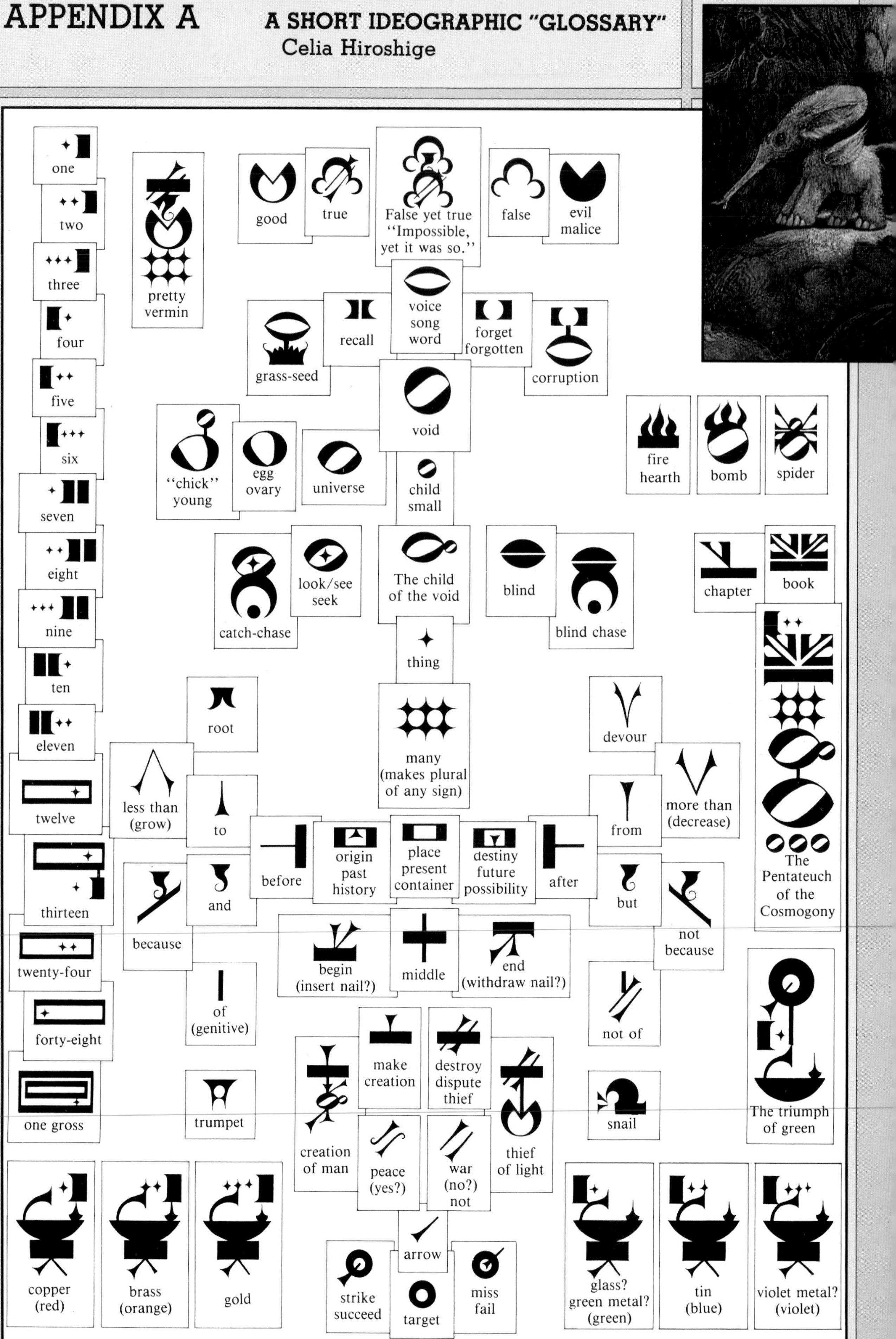
one
two
three
four
five
six
seven
eight
nine
ten
eleven
twelve
thirteen
twenty-four
forty-eight
one gross
pretty vermin
good
true
False yet true "Impossible, yet it was so."
false
evil malice
grass-seed
recall
voice song word
forget forgotten
corruption
void
"chick" young
egg ovary
universe
child small
fire hearth
bomb
spider
catch-chase
look/see seek
The child of the void
blind
blind chase
chapter
book
thing
root
many (makes plural of any sign)
devour
less than (grow)
to
more than (decrease)
from
before
origin past history
place present container
destiny future possibility
after
because
and
but
not because
The Pentateuch of the Cosmogony
begin (insert nail?)
middle
end (withdraw nail?)
of (genitive)
not of
make creation
destroy dispute thief
creation of man
thief of light
trumpet
snail
The triumph of green
peace (yes?)
war (no?) not
arrow
copper (red)
brass (orange)
gold
strike succeed
target
miss fail
glass? green metal? (green)
tin (blue)
violet metal? (violet)

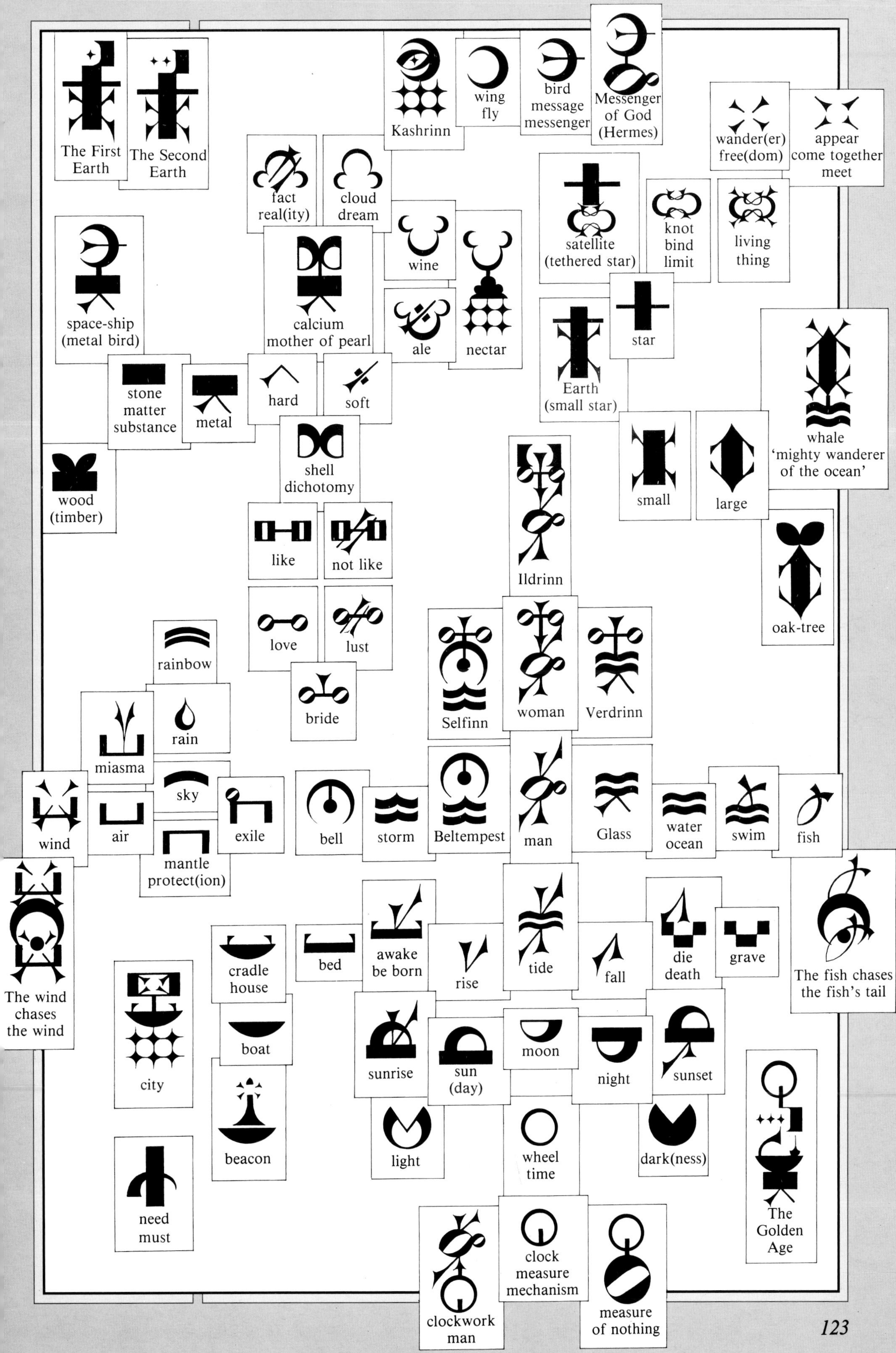
The First Earth
The Second Earth
Kashrinn
wing fly
bird message messenger
Messenger of God (Hermes)
wander(er) free(dom)
appear come together meet
fact real(ity)
cloud dream
wine
nectar
satellite (tethered star)
knot bind limit
living thing
space-ship (metal bird)
calcium mother of pearl
ale
star
Earth (small star)
whale 'mighty wanderer of the ocean'
stone matter substance
metal
hard
soft
shell dichotomy
small
large
wood (timber)
like
not like
Ildrinn
oak-tree
love
lust
bride
Selfinn
woman
Verdrinn
rainbow
rain
miasma
sky
wind
air
exile
mantle protect(ion)
bell
storm
Beltempest
man
Glass
water ocean
swim
fish
The wind chases the wind
awake be born
bed
cradle house
rise
tide
fall
die death
grave
The fish chases the fish's tail
city
boat
sunrise
sun (day)
moon
night
sunset
beacon
light
wheel time
dark(ness)
The Golden Age
need must
clockwork man
clock measure mechanism
measure of nothing

APPENDIX B

THE SOLAR PANTHEON

The six coloured moons and the six "metals" of the spectrum.

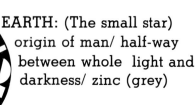

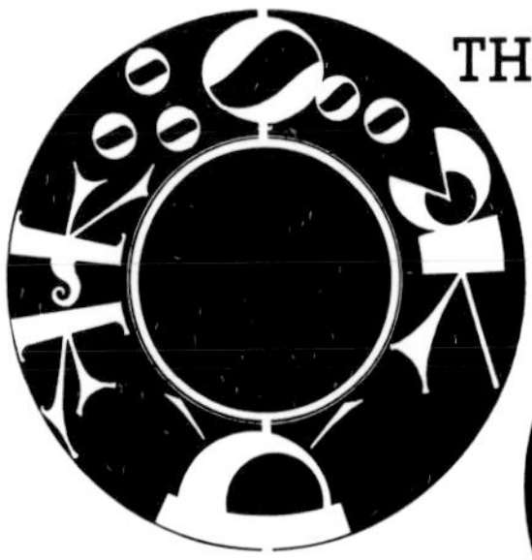

THE SUN: The first and last/ child & father/ silver (whole light)

EARTH: (The small star) origin of man/ half-way between whole light and darkness/ zinc (grey)

BELTEMPEST: The first moon/ violet metal(?) (violet-blue)

SELFINN: The second moon/ the bride of Beltempest (following in his orbit) tin (blue-torquoise)

GLASS: The third moon/ green metal (glass?) (green)

VERDRINN: The fourth moon/ the bride of Glass (following in his orbit)/ gold (yellow)

MAN: The fifth moon/ follows Ildrinn in her orbit/ zinc-Earth alloyed with copper-Ildrinn, hence brass (orange)

ILDRINN: The sixth moon/ the forgotten bride of man (leading him after Darkness)/ copper (red)

DARKNESS: The seventh moon/ the destiny of man/ the furthest moon from Earth and forever in her shadow/ lead (black)

APPENDIX C THE PENTATEUCH TODAY

Sir George Francis, *Director of Public Relations Services, U.N.T.W. and Editor of the Second Edition.*

The interpretation of the archives and their relevance to life on Earth in the 24th Century.

Although we have included many references to a *written* text — *the scribe pauses... his pen half-way to paper...* (Chapter 3) — it must be remembered that the original text of the Pentateuch was not expressed in words but in signs or ideograms. References to pen and paper occur only in those sources where the story does actually appear to have been drawn either with a pen or a brush, which seems to be supported by the accompanying symbol. Engraved tablets on the other hand are described with a very different symbol, obviously an engraver's burin in use.

Some of the ideograms obviously presented a number of problems of interpretation, simply because the objects named were of extra-terrestrial origin and therefore completely unknown to us. We cannot guess for example from what kinds of wood it was that Ildrinn (the forgotten bride of man) fashioned her deadly bow and arrows, so, using terrestrial analogues, we describe the bow as being made from yew and the arrows from hazel-withies. We have followed a similar policy when interpreting those symbols which gave us "oak", "squid", "chanterelle" etc.

Less difficult were situations where similar or related objects are represented by the same symbol. The symbol for "shell" has a large number of other interpretations. Depending on context, it may mean "shelter", "mother-of-pearl" or even — it *does* seem to depict a bivalve — a "dichotomy" or division into equal halves. Similarly the symbol for "bed" is obviously linked conceptually with that for a cradle or house, which in turn is very like the symbol for a boat. Such relationships are obvious once the story is known and we realize the important historical reasons for them. Rarely have we been forced to make wild guesses of interpretation, simply because the context usually eliminates doubt, or, where there is ambiguity, the ambiguity tends to be deliberate anyway.

We have no idea of the direction of rotation of "the First Earth" — whether their Sun rose in the East or in the West — and we get round this difficulty in the only way possible. The symbol for "sunrise" we interpret where appropriate as East, and its opposite as West, simply because that is how things are here on the "Second Earth".

The most interesting aspect of the ideographic texts is, as emphasized in the preface, what they tell us about the concepts and attitudes of the builders of the Hermes, or at least of their ancestors. They did not see fit to change anything, it seems, of the ancient texts. The Coda was all that they added. Such traditional attitudes are revealed by studying the separate ingredients of each symbol-group, the ambiguities within them and so on.

For example a city is described literally as a "meeting-place of many houses", as if houses were mobile or even capable of moving of

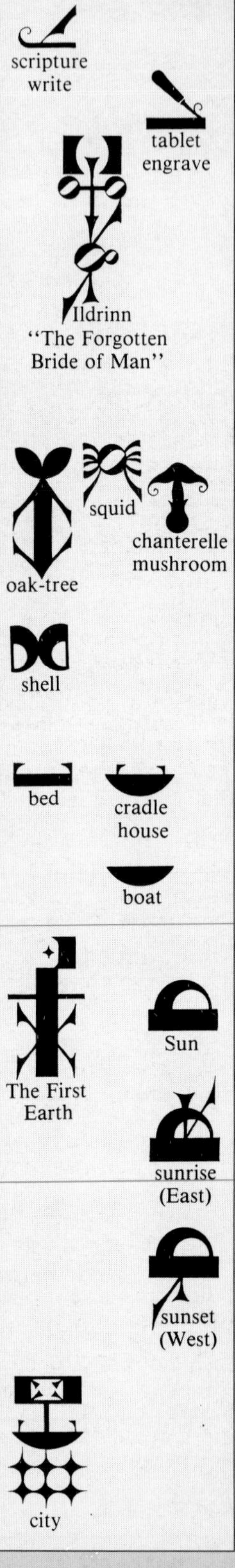

This trump-card, depicting the symbol *The end/The beginning,* typifies the deliberate ambiguities often present in the symbolic texts and images. The central ideogram as we print it here means "the end", but, when used the other way up, it also means "the beginning". The messenger comes out of darkness and from the broken rainbow (this symbol is also associated with the symbol for "grave") to the blue world and the rainbow restored. The fish/bird bears a blue sphere (the Second Earth) in its mouth.

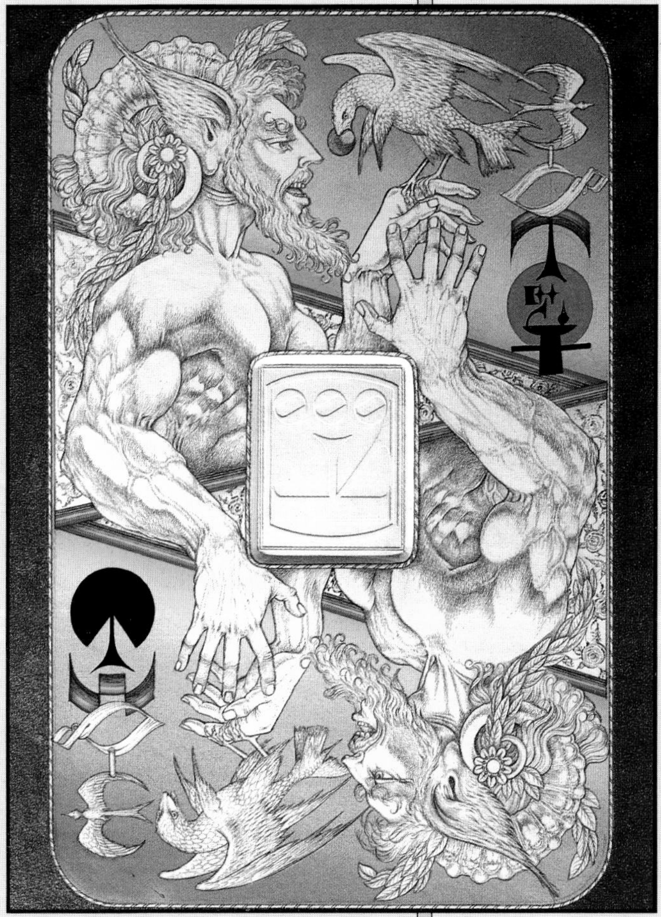

their own accord. A living thing is a "tethered wanderer", the implication perhaps being that freedom is limited or dependent. A man is represented symbolically as "the small god that rises and falls like the tides". Such examples tell us a great deal about the persistent effects of history on traditions. After all, human civilization was believed to have begun in the floating cities and in ships; such "houses" could indeed come together. Similarly, the tether which binds all living things probably originates in the notion that all the universe is dependent on God's wakefulness, that *it hangs on his thread.* Thirdly, that man's oscillatory fortunes should be linked to the tides is only to be expected when we remember his tragic isolation within the tidal ramparts of the Dry Land.

There is surely no doubt that such attitudes are implied in the symbols; our problem has only been in deciding how far to take such things. We do not wish to "read in" meanings that are not there.

It is really when we come to fundamentals that the difficulties arise. It was many months for example before we managed to interpret even the very first symbol of this edition — "things". In the original edition indeed there is no such concept, and that text begins simply with the words: *In the beginning there was less than void...* It turned out that the symbol we were having so much trouble with was related to the symbol for "many", and the interpretation was only possible after a careful contextual analysis of instances where the symbol appeared again. Obviously this is how all codes and such-like are deciphered, but in the case of the Hermes archive, the metaphysical attitudes of its authors did tend to get in the way of a purely logical approach.

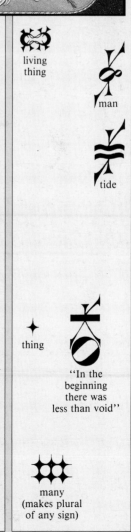

living thing

man

tide

thing

"In the beginning there was less than void"

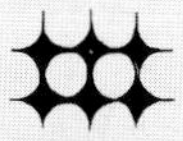

many (makes plural of any sign)

"What gold shall drip from the sparrow's beak,
when all who can sing shall learn to speak!"

As already mentioned indeed, the symbols are sometimes used almost in self-contradiction to express a paradox or a concept which is really beyond the scope of mere words. For example it is quite typical that one symbol, which we translate in Chapter 1 as "clock", should also appear elsewhere in contexts where it must represent only "machine" or "clockwork" etc. The symbol, when used for example as in the margin, obviously gives us "man of clockwork" or "automatic man". There are many such instances in which the clock symbol in no way implies measurement of time — merely mechanism. How then do we deal with a symbol which could (and perhaps *should*) be interpreted both as "measure of nothing" or as "the clock of the void". It is obviously impossible to know for sure, but fortunately some such phrases also occur in later literary (i.e. non-ideographic) works, where they are very commonly used as semi-religious "catch-phrases". Two examples of this are *clockwork toys turned their own keys* (Chapter 4), and "the wife of the man of clockwork", a description of woman which we translate perhaps rather poetically in Chapter 20 as *clockwork Columbine.* These literary sources also gave us such phrases as *midnight nursery* and the oft-repeated *We have no words.*

The point I am trying to make here is that whatever mere words we choose to represent the ideograms, there is no possibility of communicating every nuance of their meaning. The symbols which gave us such phrases as *mindless Death, blameless Earth* and so on,

clock
machine
clockwork

automatic man
(robot?)

measure
of nothing

"Clockwork toys
turned their
own keys"

"Wife of the
man of
clockwork"

midnight
nursery

"We have
no words"

Mindless
Death

are charged with oblique references to other concepts — spirit, fiction, the spectrum etc. For those who made the ideographic texts these concepts would seem inseparable, and we must learn to link them in our minds if we wish to understand the text reasonably well. Of course, to understand it thoroughly, one is obliged to learn the entire ideographic "vocabulary" and to "read" the texts for oneself.

Such phrases as *blameless Earth* bring us now to consider the moral attitudes and value judgements of the authors. How can we come to any definite conclusions on this when so many phrases are ambiguous or at the very least uncertain?

In fact I think that we can be sure that their standards of behaviour in society were very similar to our own, though there seems (for obvious reasons) to have been a much greater emphasis on an attitude which in the late twentieth and early twenty-first centuries came to be known as "green". This emerges very forcefully in the *new order* as described in the final chapter, where man is described as the *guest* rather than as the ruler of the New Earth. This attitude is also obvious from the description of the re-made Dry Land as *the commonwealth of man and beast,* and in such statements as *Green needs no evangelist. Green shall learn its own lesson.* It is however ironic that the first statement belies the very presence of Hermes itself as an evangelist of an "ecological" system of values, and that the second statement is patently disproved by the sad history of the First Earth. How fortunate we are today that such "green" attitudes are all-but universal, and that partisan colours of one sort or another are obsolete. Green has indeed learned its lesson, but not on its own. It required the Hermes for an evangelist.

Attitudes to other "anti-social" activities are tinged with this same ecologicalism. Robbery was obviously regarded as bad — Ildrinn for example is described as *the thief of light* — and yet we also find a group of symbols which we can only translate as "good thieves" or *pretty vermin,* which seems almost a contradiction in terms.

The group of symbols which represent *war* is also associated with carnivorism, cannibalism and even sexual lust. This is most evident in the sequence of images in which a burning "tiger" is transformed into a "dove" bearing a twig — could it be an olive-branch? — in its beak. Whether we should believe in the "Golden Age", when the First Earth — and indeed later the Second Earth too — are described as totally vegetarian, I am not qualified to say. However, we ourselves were of course long ago forced to adopt total veganism in order to survive the terrible famines of the twenty-first century, and our society obviously still proscribes meat-eating and cannibalism, but whether a totally vegetarian *ecology* is either possible or desirable will probably remain a subject for debate for many years to come.

It is clear that most evils were blamed on the special problems of life on the Dry Land, the tragedies of frontiers, language barriers and so on, which seem to be personified in the figure of Ildrinn. The ancient society of the people of the sea was obviously greatly admired, that is until it was destroyed later by the men themselves. A system of casual barter seems to have operated in these cities, based on mutual love and respect: *swap me a song for this bed and board,* says the

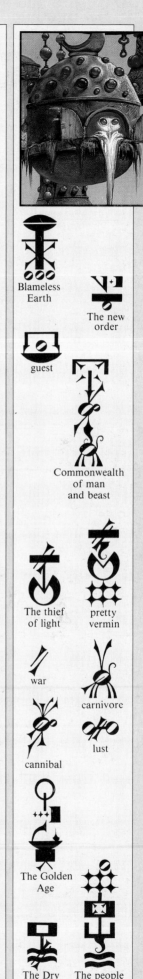

Blameless Earth

The new order

guest

Commonwealth of man and beast

The thief of light

pretty vermin

war

carnivore

cannibal

lust

The Golden Age

The Dry Land

The people of the sea

The Subtle State

fear

pain

follow
obey

Substance obedient to the will

merchant, whereas later in the last closed city even *the water was bought and sold by the measure.* The use of money seems to be regarded as squalid and ungenerous, and indeed is only mentioned after the establishment of the Last City. It is of course only *ever* needed where there is a breakdown of trust and the danger of laziness or cheating.

In sexual matters the attitudes are equally clear. Monogamy is obviously prescribed by the exhortation: *...that all the children ...shall know their own fathers and mothers and love them.* (—Chapter 20) Sodomy and pederasty are on the other hand mentioned with obvious distaste as methods of keeping down the population in the "Subtle State". It was obedience to the laws of this almost hive-like society that made it so powerful, for once an unjust and cruel régime is established through fear and pain, it is extremely difficult to topple, being totally self-perpetuating and reinforced from within. In such a "Subtle State" *personal* responsibilities and morality have no place whatsoever, for the individual is totally subservient to the state, whose only code is that of its own corporate survival. How fortunate we are today indeed that such government by fear has disappeared from the face of the Earth.

It is highly interesting however to consider the importance of the notion of "obedience" in these texts. *Substance obedient to the will* is but one of many phrases incorporating this concept, which is used to explain a great many things, from the creation itself to adaptive evolution. It is by obedience to the will for example that simple "substance" transforms itself into the whales or the fishes of the sea, and later, when the frightened animals are cursed by the loss of their speech, it is fear and need which enable them to change their shapes

and adapt themselves to a war-like and constantly-changing ecology. If they *need* sabres and knives in their mouths badly enough, then they will grow them or die. *Substance obedient to the need.*

We shall return to the concept of "obedience" later, but first I feel we should consider some other concepts which are perhaps even more important for a full understanding of the texts.

The concept of time is particularly interesting, for this is the one thing in all the texts that seems to be regarded as eternal and incapable of alteration or influence. *Not even for me shall the wheel run backwards,* says the child of the void, *nor the sand of time spring upward from the lower glass.* (— Chapter 13) Not only does time ultimately demand even the death of the gods themselves, but it is also presented paradoxically as having existed even before it existed. The clock *ticked even before it began to tick.* (— Chapter 1) Such enigmatic pronouncements are commonplace in the texts, and are often followed by the remark: *Impossible. Yet it was so.*

time

clock

Time is usually referred to as *the great wheel.* This is interesting, not only because a wheel is obviously circular and therefore unending, but also because a wheel travels at very different speeds depending upon the position of the observer. The child of the void passes at will from the *axle* to the *rim,* from an infinity of slowness to an infinity of speed. Time is, according to such a concept, not only enternal but also — "at the same time" as it were — both stationary *and* infinitely fast!

Impossible, yet it was so

Not only is it possible for him to *glimpse across the wheel of time* and see something of the future, but there is also a description of *time's mirror, where space turns in and looks upon itself* (— Chapter 14), which seems very much like a poetical description of the strange astronomical phenomenon we know today as the "white hole", the source of intense light postulated as an "entrance to another dimension". Such a mirror is indeed worthy of the gods themselves.

Conversely, there is also mention in the texts, not of a "black hole" but of something analogous. We know very well — in theory at least — that all our laws of physics would cease to apply as soon as we passed through a so-called black hole. There is surely some "place" — be it on the threshold of another universe, or between two space/time continua — where "fact" and "truth" have no meaning, for the simple reason that *anything at all is possible.* This is of course totally hypothetical, and rather uncomfortably "half-baked" too, but it is interesting to relate such way-out speculation with the description in Chapter 21 of darkness as *a horn of plenty, full of all possibilities.* It was from a dark well of infinite fictions that were chosen *the fictions that should be turned into facts.* Can we possibly suggest from this that our ancestors were capable in some way of conjuring new realities "out of thin air"? Was this another of their "lost arts"? Perhaps this might lead to another assessment of the mysterious black moon, which played such a strange part in the story. It was from its substance (Chapter 27) that the great fleet is said to have been constructed: it was *dissected... like the various pieces of a tree.* And yet there must have been more to it than that; one cannot simply cut up a whole moon and make it into space-ships. They must surely — at

The black moon
"Darkness"

that time at least — have been in command of some extremely powerful technology, engineering processes based on some strange physics we can still only guess at. Perhaps it had at least something to do with black holes. One day perhaps our researchers will give us the answer.

At all events, darkness is regarded throughout the texts as an evil, *consuming* force, the opposite of light, which *gives* — warmth, energy, life itself. The only things which are ever described as *emerging* from darkness are disease, parasitism and torture, the army of the "Subtle State" (Chapter 21).

So where do we find *the hedge between being and non-being,* or *the hole between dreaming and waking*? How might things be created *without touch, by thought alone*?

Glass makes his "palace" in just such a way. And here we may have a lead. Perhaps the answer lies in biology, in the mysterious methods by which sea-shells "make themselves" upon the backs of their tiny inhabitants. No doubt the legend of the house of Glass was based upon shells washed up on the beaches of the First Earth, and no doubt they were as much of a puzzle to our primitive ancestors as the Hermes remains to us. By what process after all — by thought, word or deed — does a sea-creature build its own shell?

There may be some clues both in the texts and in the Hermes itself, though these concepts are extremely difficult to express in lay terms and without reference to complex bio-chemical and mathematical formulae. Even the specialists only understand this in part, and any simple explanation is doomed to be only a mere shadow of the truth, a vulgarization at least preferable to total ignorance.

Whether adaptive evolution for example could ever be directed by the "will" or by "need" has been open to debate since the time of Lamarck. Even more controversial is the question of proteiformism. Did Glass really change from fish to man and back to fish again? The child of the void is described at one point as taking the shape of a man, *though his spirit could hardly hold the form, and he came and went like a ghost.* Could it be a talent of "wakefulness" — to change one's form at will? Are we in this respect simply a degenerate line of descent, unable to grasp the concept of something our ancestors knew very well, but which we just cannot do? Are we simply less "awake" than we might be, and did any such abilities still reside with the builders of the Hermes? Surely not. But then, who can rule it out? For the basic principles of evolution and D.N.A. itself would have been considered preposterous only a thousand years ago.

Let us examine the whole idea further. We are all no doubt familiar with such commonplace notions as "mind over matter", psychokinesis, psychosomatism in the treatment of disease etc. It is common practice — in some fields at least — that reality, physical "fact" or "truth", can be influenced by the exercise of the "will", a psychic force which puts us in contact and control firstly of our own bodies and ultimately to some degree of the outside world. Examples of such interaction are all around us, the foundation indeed of modern holistic medicine, the mysterious principle at work behind the useful phenomenon of clairvoyance and the conversely troublesome mystery

The hole between dreaming and waking

mind will

fact matter

of the poltergeist.

The "word" (the idea, the song) is throughout the Pentateuch a quickening thing, a command to be awake and to remain in motion. The newly-created universe is said to sing, and each star is described as *chattering to itself.* The link between word (of command) and "obedience" then is obvious, as if all life might be stripped down to this fundamental dualism. Beltempest *summons* the clouds from the sea, obedience is said to spread *like forest fire,* and his creatures need *only the song of their father for a guide.* And living is linked to some kind of command, instruction or code, and this is described most effectively in two instances. First of all when woman is created in Chapter 20: *Every part of her shape knew its place... the hidden art of all living things... a memory of its purpose. For no creature is described from outside. Only from a hidden book within...* And secondly in Chapter 22 when the forests die: *There is a thin chain that binds us all... a stairway from basement to attic, a spiral mystery that makes us one household...* Could there be a more obvious description of ecological inter-dependence and the universality of D.N.A.?

word
song
recipe
code

A thin chain
that binds
us all

A spiral
mystery

But colours need no clergy. And shall any man
tell you what is worshipful in yellow?

The palace builds the palace

tether

death

corruption

evil malice

And when we look at the bio-mechanical systems in the Hermes, who can doubt that its masters had a much greater knowledge of D.N.A. than we do? The space-ship, by some hidden code known only to them, was designed to build and repair *itself,* by processes apparently indistinguishable from those that operate when a wound heals or when a lizard's severed tail regenerates spontaneously.

We have a great deal to learn, and we have already begun. Let us only hope that such knowledge will be kept firmly under control, for the possibilities of a tragic outcome from research are just as great as the potential benefits. Knowledge may be worth having for its own sake, but only too often does it bring with it apparently beneficial technological advances which eventually prove to have been against our best interests. So, whatever we discover, we must always obey the first rule of the *new order — that we know the consequences first as far as we may. And it shall be done slowly, with watchfulness.* (Chapter 31)

This principle of self-building was also described very briefly in connection with the floating cities, where *palaces built themselves, not stone upon stone, but from the root like trees.* One can perhaps go so far as understanding how this might happen, but to discover the mechanism or the "word" which made it happen is another matter entirely. How indeed was the process initiated? How was it prescribed or designed? How was it maintained? How was it guided?

Preposterous as it may seem, we can only conclude — in lay terminology at least — that the people of the floating cities and the masters of the Hermes were capable of manipulating the D.N.A. by some kind of "psychic" means. Not only that, they must also have been capable of controlling such living (and partly-living!) systems by purely psychic methods too. One has only to make a thorough search of the Hermes to discover that it has no mechanical control systems whatsoever, no buttons to push, no switches, no levers, and the vastly complicated network of "nerve pathways", although leading inevitably to a central point or "control cell", do not lead us to anything analogous to a brain at all. The whole system *must* have been controlled purely by thought or "will", driven through space and planetary atmospheres perhaps as effortlessly as a man might use his own limbs for walking — by almost unconscious mental control. What became of such technology after they landed on the Second Earth is a controversial topic. At all events it is obvious that *the art was a lost art* for whatever reason. And whether we should try to find it again is also open to debate.

There are many more instances in the text where the idea or the "word" precedes the reality, where life depends on awareness or wakefulness (the open eye) and on the tether of memory (the thread). Loss of awareness, a tendency to sleep and forget, are all-pervasive in the books, and inevitably linked with concepts of Death (*I am forgetfulness,* says Death in Chapter 30), disease (*My recipe for corruption. Here is how,* says the dead wife of Glass in Chapter 24) and evil (*beasts without minds... blind torturers every one ...* thus is the "Subtle State" described in Chapter 21).

There is surely a sense in which this attitude is patent truth, for is death anything more than the point at which the body forgets how to maintain itself? Is not disease — simply put — nothing more than a lack of bodily communication, a corporal "disobedience" or lethargy? And surely evil itself is nothing more than anti-life, a breakdown of codes or a forgetting of rules. The word "evil" itself, even in our own language, is merely — though perhaps not coincidentally — an anagram of "live". And although living things are represented as self-motivated, i.e. *turning their own keys,* they are also described as "tethered wanderers", free only within certain limitations. The world too is automatic but dependent, *hanging by his thread* — relying on an overall force of "wakefulness" that keeps the universe in being. Without wakefulness or care (the open eye), we degenerate into *physical* disobedience (disease, death etc.) and *mental* disobedience, which is best exemplified by the curse of the forgotten tongues, when both men and animals suddenly found themselves unable to communicate with each other. Once again, it all comes down to communication, to a code, to the "word".

The word sign (voice, song, story etc.) is also linked with the symbol for "seed", which varies from case to case, literally "the story of (or recipe for!) and oak-tree", "the song (or code-word) of the grass". The great tragedy of the first landing on the Dry Land was not only the loss of life. Equally lamentable was the loss of seed and grain, bemoaned in similar terms to those used when the precious libraries of the sea-people were scuttled. The destruction of information — records, history etc. — is tantamount to destroying lives, for it not only wipes away all achievement, but also the lessons of experience which might be a guide for the future.

So the Hermes itself might be regarded as the ultimate "seed", a store-house of precious information upon which the future of the Second Earth depends utterly. Once again the *word* is all-important for *life.*

Another interesting group of symbols is that concerned with fiction. The symbol for a cloud — not surprisingly — also represents a sheep. However it also must be interpreted in other contexts as "dream", "whim", "fiction", "lie", even "spirit". The act of creation is often described as *substance obedient to the whim,* but the insubstantial children of Beltempest, who need only light and air for their sustenance, must surely be *spirits* rather than whims. Strangely enough, the symbol needs only to be inverted, and it has a totally different, though not unrelated, meaning — wine. And here again is another set of ideas. What we translate as *ale* is merely "soft wine", *nectar* is literally "wine of flowers", and *honey* is "wine of bees". So you can understand how the same symbol can also be used to mean "sweet", "nourishing" and even "intoxicating". The connection between drunkenness, sleep and dreams therefore brings us in a full circle.

But you may — understandably — be uneasy. Could not a symbol such as the one which we have translated as *the flocks of Beltempest* also be interpreted with equal logic as "the many lies of Beltempest", thus making a totally different story? Indeed such alternatives could conceivably be correct, but we believe it is doubtful. We must after all

tethered wanderer (living thing)

The open eye look/see seek

acorn

grass-seed

cloud sheep dream

wine

ale

nectar

honey

The flocks of Beltempest

and in the last resort rely on our own judgement. We do inevitably choose the interpretation which fits best not only with the images and with the non-ideographic texts, but also with our own ideas and minimal prejudices! So please accept this interpretation as valid — at least as valid as a linguistic interpretation ever could be — for we have debated all doubtful points long and hard, and we have no interest in deception or misrepresentation.

Let us continue now with an examination of some other interesting aspects of the texts, both metaphysical and quasi-religious.

Great importance is attached throughout to considerations of number. *We counted only as far as one,* it says in Chapter 31, *One Earth. One people. One world.* This is an important statement, for in the earlier chapters a religious significance is particularly attached to the number three. In declaring *one world,* they were in fact abandoning old religions, renouncing out-dated attitudes. The old trinity was broken. There was neither Beltempest nor Glass on the Second Earth — only the third brother, man. We shall deal later on with this and the various other threefold divisions, but first I should like to examine the rôle of the fundamental dualism involved in the story, the dynamic dichotomy which is represented throughout as a blind chase in a dream-wood. *The games were already ages old,* it says in Chapter 3. The symbols "catch-chase" and "blind-chase", which we have rendered on one occasion as *catch as catch can* and *blind man's buff,* crop up over and over again to describe the Satyr's pursuit of the nymph, the wind chasing the wind, the fish pursuing the fish's tail. It seems to represent the basic life-giving polarities of a dynamic universe, manifest in such things as the poles of magnetism, the forces we call Ying Yang and above all in the all-pervasive dichotomy of sex — the ultimate polarity.

A similar dualism is evident in attitudes to light and dark, obviously equated with good and bad, life and death. The first created thing is in fact light, and the worst thing that can happen to the universe is darkness. *Sleep no more,* says the newly-created black moon, *lest darkness be the lot of all.* (— Chapter 5) The two are represented physically by the Sun, described as a white ox, and by the moon *Darkness,* forever in the shadow of the Earth. And the Earth, being half-way between light and dark (and between good and evil) is inevitably represented as *grey, the colour of dull zinc.* Ildrinn is the queen of darkness simply because there was *no heritage for her in the light.* All her powers came from negative forces; she is *the thief of light*, and on her trump-card her attributes are the "darkness projector" and the snuffing-hood.

Incidentally, in connection with the "darkness projector" I should perhaps mention the recent sensational researches aboard the Hermes. It now seems apparent from various artifacts and documentation discovered there that some unknown technique enabled light to be absorbed and concentrated, rather like a laser acting in reverse. These artifacts do indeed appear to be weapons, and were apparently designed to have devastating effects, completely absorbing all energies — light, heat, etc. — and perhaps ejecting it

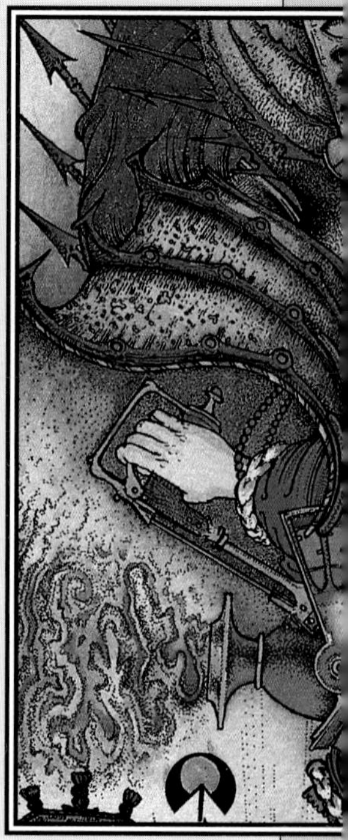

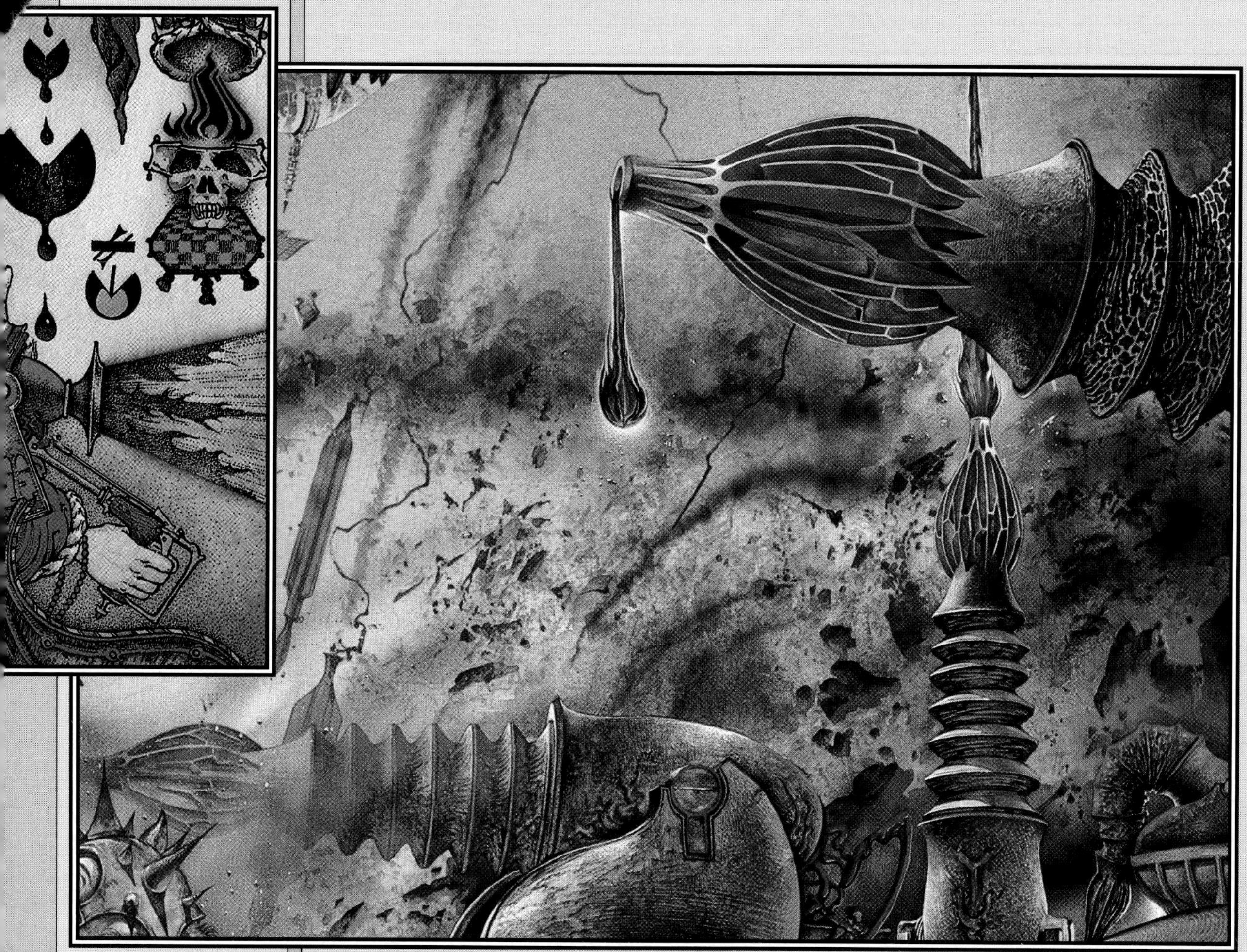

harmlessly into some other dimension. Preposterous talk maybe, but the relics are there for all to examine. It is obvious too from historical records that such weapons were indeed used in some early and disastrous attempts to colonize hostile planets. Fortunately *we* now no longer need such weapons, and perhaps we should leave such technologies safely un-researched, for maybe the knowledge of them could somehow re-establish a need for their use.

Three circles end statement

thing

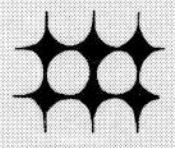

many

The most recurrent instance of the importance of number is, as I said earlier, the repeated division into three. Not only is each ideographic statement rendered complete only by a row of three small circles, but the entire system of counting is also based on three. Then, by doubling, there are six sacred metals, six coloured moons, and the symbol for "many" consists of a six-fold repetition of the symbol for "thing".

The "first" or primary colours — blue, yellow and red — are three in number. In painting, any colour may theoretically be made from these simple ingredients, and the lithographic process used to print this book is also based on this principle. For our distant ancestors however, these colours also had great religious significance, violet/blue for the kingdom of the sky, green/yellow for the deep, and orange/red for the Dry Land. Each moon also has a colour and the name of a divinity attached to it (— See Appendix B *The Solar Pantheon*), and it does seem from photographic archival material that the moons did indeed appear in the sky in these colours. A strange landscape indeed.

It is also interesting to note that the wheel of time itself is described as being three-coloured like a rainbow, and it is from the three-coloured rainbow that comes the promise in Chapter 30 — *You have come to your own place and shall never leave it.* Three moreover is the number of the horns of Glass and of course of the three "kingdoms" of land, air and water, which are symbolized in representations of the child of the void by the physical attributes of horns, wings and fish's tail respectively.

Three permeates the entire literature. There are three so-called "colour litanies", e.g. *But colours need no clergy. And shall any man tell you what is worshipful in yellow?* applied to each primary colour in turn, though in the end all seem to be over-ruled by the triumph of green. *Need any man be told which colour is king?*

Colours need no clergy

The triumph of green

Need any man be told which colour is king?

Consideration of the six colours and the six moons brings us now to the vexed question of the tides. The moons — and the Sun, for that matter — are likened to oxen or beasts of burden, that *hauled the seething waters across the flat lands, sometimes higher, sometimes lower.* This must surely be an under-statement, for our computer researchers have tried very hard to simulate the tidal effects of seven — only very modest — hypothetical digital moons on a hypothetical digital ocean. Whatever the orbits, the effects are repeatedly catastrophic, peaking every now and again in what in reality would be enormously destructive super-tides. No civilization would be viable under such conditions except on very high land, and it would then be practically impossible to establish harbours or communication with any sea-borne population. Cliffs would be monstrous barriers to the sea, as would estuaries etc. However, apart from all these considerations, heated controversy still rages among our astrophysicists as to whether a system with seven moons is possible at all, particularly when one of them (*Darkness*) is described as being in a state of perpetual eclipse. We shall never know the truth of course, for the First Earth must now be at least hundreds of light-years distant.

Be that as it may, it is interesting to point out again the similarity between the symbol for man ("rising and falling small god") and for tide ("rising and falling ocean"). No doubt the tempestuous destiny of man was indelibly linked with his first disastrous attempts to settle the Dry Land.

The importance of the tides must have been enormous, that is unless the people of the Dry Land remained completely cut off from all commerce with the people of the sea. This latter scenario does seem to be supported by the history, which makes no further mention of the people of the sea until their floating cities are finally plundered following the tragic spoliation of the land.

Another important concept in the literature is that of *the sacred place where air and water meet.* The surface of the sea — that vigorous "interface" between air and water — seems to have been regarded with enormous reverence, and this is probably not surprising when you remember that the first civilization floated on the sea *like lilies on a lake.* The very fact of floating must have seemed miraculous to them, indeed it was the one law of physics to which they most obviously owed their survival and prosperity. Before the Dry Land was made, anything that did not float was in danger of being lost forever, and an entire civilization seems to have been built up without metal or stone, all its materials being utterly biological in origin. Whether such a thing is possible is yet another point of argument, and yet we do have considerable historical evidence in the archives that such a civilization did in fact exist, though as we know all its heritage was destroyed by man himself.

The surface of the sea is also important for another reason, for it was here that the mysterious "purple shells" appeared, which proved to contain the *Kashrinn,* the eventual *mothers of men.* This part of the story has understandably given rise to considerable discussion. What were these mysterious creatures? Did they perhaps come from somewhere else in the universe? Were they visitors from another

man

tide

The tide comes in

The tide turns

The place where air and water meet

Kashrinn

planet — colonists indeed? All we can know for sure is that the whole question of man's origin was (and still is today) the cause of endless debate, scientific argument and religious squabbling. This is quite throroughly dealt with in our notes explaining the break in Chapter 14, but we made no mention there of the ancient sects and factions which seem to have quarrelled over this for centuries, debating whether man needed a father to beget him. Could it have been Beltempest? they ask (*Beltempest keeps them. They are his.* — Chapter 14), or perhaps even the child of the void himself? Such debate is at all events as irrelevant today as it ever was, and surely none of us could possibly accept any of this as fact. Man's origin is certainly unknown, but none of these suggestions dispel the mystery.

More important controversies rage — sufficient argument to keep us busy with historical fact rather than with fanciful legend. Let us confine our thoughts now to more reasonable questions.

What for example happened all those thousands of years ago once the huge space-fleet had landed on the Second Earth? And why is there no trace of the fleet today — neither in our own histories nor in the fossil record? According to the texts, at least a thousand ships landed, each one the size of a city. Yet nothing remains, not a spar nor a cooking-pot — not even so much as a nail.

Until we made thorough studies of the Hermes itself, this question seemed to cast a shadow of doubt over the whole account. Was it all just an elaborate lie? Surely not. Anyway, as soon as the bio-mechanical systems of the Hermes were better understood, we had an obvious and complete answer to the riddle. For the Hermes is — and no doubt all other ships of the fleet were — not only bio-mechanical, but also totally bio-degradable. The truth of it was that the fleet simply rotted away, devoured by the microbes, fungi, insects and so on that were on Earth before them. *Her ways are not our ways,* as it says in Chapter 31. The New Earth was "subtle" indeed, and no doubt the fleet ceased to exist in a matter of years rather than centuries.

The story was no doubt passed on from generation to generation, but who can say in how few centuries such history would come to be regarded as sheer fantasy, discarded as absurd, irrelevant. So this was why the Hermes was preserved, safe (ironically) only in the sterile vacuum of space, waiting through the untold millennia till man should come again into space and learn of his own long-forgotten history. And the only thoroughly inorganic artifacts we found there were of course the copper and gold tablets upon which the Pentateuch had been engraved. Even these would not have been safe on Earth. They had no alternative but to preserve their messenger in space, safe from all threat of plunder, ignorance and decay.

And here again is the triumph of green re-affirmed. In the dynamic of life no riches are safe from the corruption of "moth and rust". Only in Heaven should our riches be stored up. Perhaps that one small message has penetrated even through all those millennia of human history and pre-history. Somehow we always seemed to know there was *something* waiting for us out there among the stars. And the message from Heaven is indeed a message of eternal life, for the triumph of green is the triumph of life.

So lastly we come to one of the most baffling things of all. We said earlier that the Hermes was utterly deserted. There was no trace of man nor beast. Her crew had simply disappeared. And yet there is, as you must already know, one very special "cell" that is no less deserted, but in a very different way. It is lined with delicate fabrics of soft and colourful weave, its walls are chased with amazingly complex patterns of circuits and "nerve pathways". It is for all the world like the cell of a queen bee, yet vastly more complex, and above the strangely small, almost man-size door, is this simple ideographic inscription: *The forgotten bride of man — remembered in the end.*

The forgotten bride of man — remembered in the end

Could it be that Ildrinn actually existed — as physically as you and I — eating, sleeping, ruling her now well-loved subjects with benevolence and compassion? Or perhaps the story is simply an allegory based on a dynasty of mortal queens, her union with the child of the void nothing more than a poetical way of representing her physical death?

What does it matter? Surely there is nonetheless a sense in which all fictions are fact, all lies truth. The makers of the Hermes would certainly have understood that paradox, and perhaps we have a lot to learn from them about the fundamental contradictions inherent in the very fabric of the universe itself.

Impossible. We have no words

And so her cell remains a shrine. Thousands visit it every day, gaze at her couch in wonder. For this is the hollow tree that hummed like an organ-loft. Here she lay *as naked as a pillow,* the bride of God himself. As the scriptures put it, over and over: *Impossible. We have no words.*

The End